2004

ONCE UPON A RHYME

IMAGINATION FOR A NEW GENERATION

Poems From The South

Edited by Donna Samworth

 Young**Writers**

First published in Great Britain in 2005 by:
Young Writers
Remus House
Coltsfoot Drive
Peterborough
PE2 9JX
Telephone: 01733 890066
Website: www.youngwriters.co.uk

SB ISBN 1 84460 651 1

Foreword

Young Writers was established in 1991 and has been passionately devoted to the promotion of reading and writing in children and young adults ever since. The quest continues today. Young Writers remains as committed to engendering the fostering of burgeoning poetic and literary talent as ever.

This year's Young Writers competition has proven as vibrant and dynamic as ever and we are delighted to present a showcase of the best poetry from across the UK. Each poem has been carefully selected from a wealth of *Once Upon A Rhyme* entries before ultimately being published in this, our twelfth primary school poetry series.

Once again, we have been supremely impressed by the overall high quality of the entries we have received. The imagination, energy and creativity which has gone into each young writer's entry made choosing the best poems a challenging and often difficult but ultimately hugely rewarding task - the general high standard of the work submitted amply vindicating this opportunity to bring their poetry to a larger appreciative audience.

We sincerely hope you are pleased with our final selection and that you will enjoy *Once Upon A Rhyme Poems From The South* for many years to come.

Contents

Jessica Pleace (10)   62
Rebecca Brayne (11)   63
Jodie Macfarren (10)   64
Shannen Behan (10)   64
Charlotte Boulton (10)   65
Joe Difford (10)   65
Emma Clark (10)   66
Sharmaine Hughes (10)   66
Danielle Rickard (10)   67
Rosie Wallis (10)   67
Samantha Dance (10)   68
Ryan Henry (10)   68
Daniel John (10)   69
Philip Hellmuth (10)   69
Ben Wolfe (10)   70
Daimion Smith (10)   70
Zoe Sharp (10)   71
Kane Rose (10)   71
Clara Millar (10)   72

Culverstone Green CP School, Gravesend

Chloe Humphrey (10)   72
Steven Wincott (10)   73
Shane Brown (10)   73
Samuel Stevens (10)   73
Hannah Stokes (10)   74
Sam Bampton (10)   74
Kathryn Tye (10)   74
Sophie Ballard (10)   75
Glen Harrison (10)   75
Oscar Saxton (10)   75
Adam Stonham (10)   76
Bryony Stokes (10)   76
Matthew Coward (10)   76
Melissa Kose (10)   77
Rebecca Pillet (10)   77
Anna Johnson (10)   77
Rickie Durnall (10)   78

East Wittering Community Primary School, Chichester

Ryan McManus (10)	78
Amber Macdonald (10)	79
Ryan Parfoot (10)	79
Georgia Heath (10)	79
Sarah Bevis (10)	80
Chloe Stanton (10)	80
Jade Hawkins (10)	80
Jonathan Manuel (10)	81
Charlie Ames (11)	81
Gavin Ngo (10)	81
Ben Houghton (10)	82
Billy Callow (11)	82
Lauren Taylor (10)	83
Daniel Fuller (10)	83
George Taylor (10)	83
Melissa Bearham (11)	84
Emma Napper (10)	84
Sammy-Jo Valler (10)	85
Alex Heath (10)	85
Elliott Courtney (10)	85
Portia Bye (10)	86

Hampton Hill Junior School, Hampton Hill

Alexander Loveday (10)	86
Serena Dias (10)	87
Jack Ravenscroft (10)	87
Scott Mitchell (10)	88
Harriet Thomlinson (10)	88
Georgia Cottington (10)	89
Luke Beer (10)	89
Susan Jonusas (10)	90
Jessica Roe (10)	90
Sophie Dexter (10)	91
Adam Bassett (11)	91
Thomas Gellatly (10)	92
George Thompson (10)	92
James Boultbee (11)	93
Giada Ciccozzi (10)	93
Jonny Brown (11)	94
Alex Cheah (10)	94

Hawes Down Junior School, West Wickham

Tegan Giannandrea (8)	95

Holy Trinity CE Primary School, Cookham

Lewis Green (10)	95
Rebecca Price (10)	96
Rhys Palmer (10)	96
Kiren Sehota (10)	97
Christopher Benge (10)	97
Daisy Green (10)	98
Alastair Beveridge (10)	98
Jennifer Crichton (10)	99
Craig Jenkins (10)	99
Rachel Brand (10)	100
Lizzie Davis (10)	101
Lindsay Coulson (10)	102
Harvey Dale (10)	103
Carmen Ip (10)	104
Hannah Wallace (10)	105
Sam Taylor (10)	106
Charlie Breden (10)	107
Michelle Watt (10)	108
Elizabeth Ferguson (10)	109
John Cousins (11)	110
Josh Baker (10)	111
Corey McAllen (11)	112
Megan Treacy (10)	113
Natan Bram (10)	114
Hiroki Takano (10)	115
Elizabeth Chalmers (10)	116
Zoe Broadbent (10)	117

Middleton Cheney Primary School, Banbury

Joshua Palmer (10)	117
Christopher Pridmore (10)	118
Sharni Carrier (10)	119
Lee Harris (8)	119
Maddie Knight (8)	120
Sarah Blair (9)	120
Rachel Hoose (8)	121
Rebecca Hyseni (10)	122

Rosherville CE Primary School, Gravesend

Olatejumola Ogunlana (8)	122
Alister Brown (8)	122
Alisha Baker (9)	123
Monica Randhawa (10)	123
Matthew Ball (10)	123
Harjot Bahia (9)	124
Thomas Osmond (10)	124
Marie-Louise Svaleng (10)	124
Becky Brown (10)	125
Selina Rathore (10)	125
Martin Brown (10)	125
Aman Oberai (10)	126
Jodie Felstead (10)	126
Luke Mancini (10)	126
Chloe Fry (9)	127
Maisie Osmond (9)	127
Ashley Ollek Adams (9)	127
Olabambo Ogunlana (10)	128

Sacred Heart School, Wadhurst

Katie Akehurst (9)	128
Peter Carvalho (9)	128
Lily Parham (9)	129
Elinor Bushell (9)	129
Jasmine Oliver (10)	130
Cameron Levy (9)	130
Amalia Austin (9)	130
Sophie Rist (10)	131
Rebecca Lennon (9)	131
Ben Attenborough (9)	131
Anthony St John-Bond (10)	132
Lauren-Nicole Little (10)	132
Holly Turner (9)	132
Eleanor Boylan (9)	133
Andrew Horsfall-Turner (10)	133
William Pearson (10)	133
Oriel Bathurst (10)	134
Joseph Sandford (10)	134
Georgia Sanderson-Nash (10)	134

Valerie Van Riet (9)	135
Joshua Spencer (9)	135

The Holy Family RC Primary School, Maidstone

Anthony Hill (10)	135
Megan Fisher (10)	136
Jake Brown (10)	136
Cameron Kellett (10)	137
Kevin Kerr (10)	137
Alex Hobbs (10)	138
Ashley Peavey (10)	138
Emily Dixon (10)	139
Roxanne Parker (10)	139
Samuel Cooksley (10)	140
Aliye Aker (10)	140

West Hove Junior School, Hove

Verity McGhie (8)	140
Alex Goodger-Marsh (7)	141
Charlie Byard (7)	141
Sommer Ballagher (7)	141
Isobel Crookston (7)	141
Lois Selmes (7)	142
Nancy Wheeler (7)	142
Billy Davis (7)	142
Sam Cissell (7)	142
Harry Harris (7)	143
Joe Miller-Marshall (8)	143
Michael Gaffney (7)	143
Isaac Squires (8)	144
Ethan Berry (7)	144
Violet McGhie (8)	144
Jade Ford (7)	145
Matthew Mill (7)	145
Noshin Ahmed (7)	145
Layla Sattar (8)	146
Jay Fry (7)	146
Sophie Odwell (7)	146
Charlie Holden (7)	147
Alice Cropper (7)	147
Louis Howell (7)	147

The Poems

A Monstrous Poem

There was a monster that came to town,
It was very big and very round.
We heard it stomping like an earthquake.
We formed a team,
We chased it off across the stream.
We cornered it behind the bandstand
But it wouldn't budge.
I reached out and touched it,
It felt like sludge . . .

We wanted to make it go away,
We chased it around the town all day.
It roared and bellowed like a beast in pain.
There was a clap of thunder and it started to rain,
With that, the monster started off towards the school.
The headmaster thought it was an April fool.
We cornered it behind the science block,
I reached out and touched it,
It felt like rock . . .

There was a big bang and the monster ran,
We gave chase,
But it was getting dark as the monster headed towards the park.
We thought up a plan to set a trap,
But before we could do it,
The monster saw right through it
And jumped in the lake, which was a big mistake
Because he could not swim.
Poor old him!

Alex Hart (10)
Bickley Park School, Bickley

The Last Stand

The ground is filled with blood
It's almost as if there's a flood
They will chop off your head
And then you'll be dead
But what a flood of blood

Sometimes you wish you were dead
You'd gladly chop off your head
You'd go to Hell
And then ring a bell
But still you'd have lost your head

But suddenly you have some hope
Even though you can't see the pope
You'd get in the fray
But get chopped away
And now you know there's no hope.

Freddy Catterall (9)
Bickley Park School, Bickley

Nature Watches

As the stream runs in the creak,
As trees rustle in the autumn wind,
Nature watches,
As the squirrel eats,
As the mouse squeaks,
Nature watches,
As a person opens a gate,
I quietly think to myself,
How much can this take?

Drew Davis (10)
Bickley Park School, Bickley

I Love Football!

I love to play sport
Football's the best,
One day I hope
To pass the test.

To be a footballer
A famous one,
I hope one day
I'll say, 'We've won!'

Along with my teammates
We'll be so proud,
The crowd will be cheering
Ever so loud.

One day I'll score
The winning goal,
Beckham's position
I will have stole.

I'll play for Chelsea
The greatest team,
We'll beat Arsenal
That's my dream.

Jourdan Kirby (10)
Bickley Park School, Bickley

Food

When I look into the fridge at night
I open the door and get a fright
I see squashed tomatoes
And crusty potatoes
I look around for somewhere clean
Just to get a decent cuisine
Broccoli and Brussels
Also smelly mussels

Now I look on section two
Hoping to find something new
But there's nothing but mouldy meat
Rotten cheese that smells like feet
All I want is something to feast on
At this time of the night

Then I look onto the bottom shelf
Sweets from Heaven that ruin my health
Candyfloss galore!
Chocolate more and more
Liquorice, bubblegum, all the rays of the sun
Wobbly jelly that is fun
Now I take all I can find
Hoping that my mum will not mind.

Arin Remzi (10)
Bickley Park School, Bickley

A Bird In The Sky

In the dark shadows of the willow trees,
I sat down and hugged my knees,
I gazed up at the sky,
Which seemed so high,
Oh! How I wish I could fly,
Like a bird in the sky.

I fell into a trance
And dreamt I could dance,
Like the birds in the sky,
Who fly so high,
Oh! How I wish I could fly,
Like a bird in the sky.

As the gentle breeze shook me awake,
I could feel my neck ache
And, as I saw the ground,
I slowly came around,
Oh! How I wish I could fly,
Like the birds in the sky.

Rahul Amin (10)
Bickley Park School, Bickley

The Knight

There was a big black knight
That came out at midnight
He always gave me a terrible scare

And then one night in the dense cold fog
I heard the painful howl of a dog
Till the knight had helped it in its pain

I never saw the knight again
I guess he wasn't so bad
Now I feel sorry and sad
He only came because he wanted a friend.

Alex Czepliewicz (10)
Bickley Park School, Bickley

The Leprechaun

There was a young leprechaun from Dublin
Who when he played rugby was sinbinned
His real name was Jack
He had a bad back
All this made his bad mother grin

For some reason on his back there was a fin
This interfered with his spine and his chin
This made his mind black
He ate Tic-Tacs
This made him throw the javelin

He was somehow drawn to a pin
He used it to play the violin
He lived in a cul-de-sac
Which made him a maniac
After this he was like a goblin.

Michael Jones (10)
Bickley Park School, Bickley

The Sun

The sun shines down on us,
But doesn't make a very big fuss,
When it gets sad, it makes us mad,
By pouring water on our heads.

When it gets hot,
It makes us very cross,
When we get sweat all over our body,
But it should be very sorry.

When it shines through the windows,
It doesn't help me watch my videos,
But it does help me play,
By making a wonderful day.

Max Judge (10)
Bickley Park School, Bickley

The Spanish Flea

There was a little Spanish flea
He was a rock star but had a bad knee
It really did hurt
So he boomed 'Alert' and never played music again

There was a little Spanish flea
And after his very bad knee
He changed his job
But became a slob
What a very sad flea was he

There was a little Spanish flea
He started to play some rugby
But he got maloshed
Because he was squashed
And never played rugby again

And that's his-tory!

Duncan Marrett (10)
Bickley Park School, Bickley

A Stranger In The Night

A stranger was outside my house last night,
No one knew who he was or where he came from,
He had a brown coat, a brown hat
And eyes as dark as the midnight sky.

Some strange things went on that night,
That dark, cold, misty night he walked off,
As if he was looking for someone but was out of luck.

Nothing else went on that night,
The street stayed quiet and bare
And nothing ever went on like that ever again
And the man was never to return.

William Northwood (11)
Bickley Park School, Bickley

The Bug

The bug creeps round and round and round,
Over every mound in the ground and
Down!
She spots a creature lurking in the ground.
The bug enters and she sees,
Crawling up her hairy knees,
A spider,
With *big* yellow eyes,
Staring in the pitch-black.
The bug crept
And stepped
Around the hole,
Where she met a mole
And they all had a drink,
Which made them all go pink.

Matthew Squires (10)
Bickley Park School, Bickley

An Edinburgh Night

An Edinburgh night is an entirely different thing from the day.
That bagpipes have stopped, everyone is supposedly sleeping.
But do not expect a quiet night.
The drumming of the rain against the window
The crashing of thunder as it leaves the cloud it built upon,
The constant attack of midges biting your bare skin,
The trains rattling in the distance,
The cars whizzing past the rows of houses,
The owls hooting as if it was still the middle of the day,
The loud footsteps of drunk men shouting as they walk
                              down the dirty paths,
The dogs barking and howling.
No wonder I cannot fall asleep.

Christopher Bowdler (11)
Bickley Park School, Bickley

Seasons Tanka

When in the springtime
And the flowers are growing
The sunshine golden
You are feeling so alive
It could stay like this forever

When in the summer
And the fruit has ripened
The bees are flying
The swallows glide through the air
We wish it would never end . . .

When in the autumn
And many leaves are falling
Trees brown and orange
The days are getting shorter
The winter is almost here . . .

When in the winter
And the birds are migrating
The ground is snow-covered
With hot log fires indoors . . .
A year's worth of seasons.

Michael Moore (10)
Bickley Park School, Bickley

The Dark Knight

The dark knight
hidden with might
hid in the Satan park,
waiting for the shark.

The stream gleamed
with the moonbeam.
Dangerous sites
waited in the stream.

At last it came out
ready and hungry
not knowing was going to get slain.
It looked around smelling him out.

The dark knight
pounced out
killing the dangerous shark
all that just in a night.

All that would happen again
next night in the moonlight,
another shark ready to go out
will get slain by that dark knight.

Edouard Whyte (12)
Bickley Park School, Bickley

I Had A Friend

I had a friend called Hank
Who used to work in a bank
But his funny ideas
Made him bankrupt for years
So they knocked down his house with a tank!

I had a friend called Peter
Who went round checking the meter
But the gas did explode
While in someone's abode
Now he's underground by six metres!

I had a friend called Dave
Who liked to surf many a wave
But on one bad day
His board slid away
And he went to a watery grave!

I find it odd that all my friends
Have all, strangely, met their ends
Was it me or was it you?
Why, oh why, what did we do?

Jonathan Morris (10)
Bickley Park School, Bickley

Jokes

Young Tom Stone had always lived with his aunt,
For hours and hours he would rant and rave,
He was known to most people as a sly little brat,
As often he would steal the vicar's Sunday hat.

Young Tom Stone loved to play and joke,
Whenever he could find an unsuspecting bloke.
He would always joke all day and night,
With whatever pranks within his sight.

Young Tom Stone liked to laugh,
At any joke, however daft!
He thought one day he'd play a prank,
So he phoned the city central bank.

Young Tom Stone, 'Oh hello,' said he,
'I'd like to borrow a million pounds please.'
'Yes certainly sir, of course,' said they,
Young Tom cheered, hip hip hooray!

Young Tom Stone how happy was he,
He spent all his money, every last penny!
Until the day came for him to repay,
All the money he had borrowed that day.

Young Tom Stone, not so young anymore,
Wept and wept behind his jail cell door.
So if you ever decide to take a loan,
Just remember the story of young Tom Stone!

David Shaw (12)
Bickley Park School, Bickley

School Days Of The Week

On Monday morning I have to get up acting all cool,
But saying, 'Oh no, it's time for school.'
I go down the stairs to pack my bag
And put too many books in and it starts to sag.

Tuesday is a better day,
I see my dad go straight away.
I get out of bed and jump down the last stair,
Walk into the kitchen and sit on my chair.

Wednesday is my favourite day,
I get to paint and also play.
'It's middle of the week, where have the days gone?'
'It's nearly the end of school time, Tom.'

On Thursday mornings we have history,
Then later in the day we have geography.
There are no clubs for me today,
So I leave school early, hip hip hooray.

Friday is the last day of school,
I get something wrong and feel like a fool.
At the end of the day we hear the bell ring
And my mates and I leave school with a zing.

Toby Robinson (10)
Bickley Park School, Bickley

The Guinea Pig

The coyote had dug him up,
That is to say the guinea pig.
They had his funeral yesterday
And the fox wore his coat to the funeral.

His body was torn up, massacred,
They don't know how he died,
That is, the others, they never found out
And the fox wore his coat to the funeral.

A little one is squeaking,
That might be one of his brothers,
All the family are out now,
Staring at the massacred body
And the fox wore his coat to the funeral.

They are going back to their cave now,
Some of them will go foraging for food when it gets dark,
The guinea pig's massacred body will be left to rot and decay,
But the fox wore his coat to the funeral.

Mark Davison (11)
Bickley Park School, Bickley

Limerick

There was a young man who played cricket
He smashed the ball into his wicket
And when he was out
His face made a pout
And he hid himself in a great thicket

There was once an old man with a frown
Whose life had been turned upside-down
He had made a big bet
On the fastest horse yet
But he had lost when the jockey was thrown.

Alasdair Jones (12)
Bickley Park School, Bickley

Jumping Off The Climbing Frame

I look down on the trampoline,
My heart is pumping in my chest.

Crouching, ready, nervous and scared,
Jumping forward, arms outstretched.

Air whistles past my ears and head,
Seconds before I hit the bed.

I bounce back up and tuck my knees,
My feet go over my spinning head.

I come out of my somersault
And land standing on my feet.

Fear vanishes, I feel relief,
I climb up to do it again!

James Perry (9)
Bickley Park School, Bickley

The Match

I went to see a football match
Where dogs were playing humans,
Barky passed the ball to Patch
Who dribbled past Rob Shoeman,
A chip to Rover
Who crossed it over
To where Star jumped up to collect it,
She had a shot
Which passed Tim Dot
And went into the back of the net.
It was a goal!
The dogs had scored
And with that the match ended.

James Brooks (10)
Bickley Park School, Bickley

My Pet

I have a pet
That lives in a cage
And doesn't have a name
She sleeps in the day
And runs at night as if she's in a game
She's black and yellow
And usually mellow
Unless she's aggravated
Her food is alive, she eats a lot
She's been patient and waited
As I only feed her three times a week
And leave cleaning her cage until it starts to reek
She spends a lot of time laying in the dark
She's not the kind of pet
I can walk around the park
Now my poem is complete
My pet I can reveal
A scaly leopard gecko with skin like orange peel!

James Turner (10)
Bickley Park School, Bickley

Over The Top!

Over the top, over the top!
We're going over the top!
Oh no we're going on to fight
Just before the dawn of light
We're going to be tired
And inspired
To win this battle alone
To make this zone
All our own
We're going over the top!

Alex Bear (10)
Bickley Park School, Bickley

The Circus

I wanted to go to the circus,
I wanted to go today,
I asked my mother
And she said yes,
Then we were on our way.

We got in the car
And sat down straight,
We studied the map,
Off at last,
I never like being late.

We arrived at the circus,
We sat on the seat,
We ordered some popcorn,
Some nuts and a drink
And hungrily began to eat.

We saw the clown
And the super stampede,
The big cat with its mighty roar,
I was feeling a big frightened,
Did the lion want its feed?

When the head of the clowns
Was covered in goo,
We all shouted and screamed,
But I kept my head down,
I didn't want the same too.

We left the circus,
Discussing our day,
We jumped in the car,
It was dark, cold and damp,
But we were on our way.

James Reeves (10)
Bickley Park School, Bickley

The Shadow Master

The Shadow Master came my way,
I never knew what happened.
He came so quickly and was gone,
Life will never be the same.

All happiness was drained away,
Everything I knew was not the same.
My family and friends,
Gone forever from my sight.

Seeing nothing, what a bore,
Just thinking what happened.
Not knowing where I'm going,
Life will never be the same.

Blindness is a punishment,
It's some kind of torture.
Why, why, why pick me?
I have a life of things to see.

The Shadow Master came my way,
I never knew what happened.
He came so quickly and was gone,
Life will never be the same.

Kiran Preddy (11)
Bickley Park School, Bickley

Feet

When you're young they bounce along,
Where you want to go,
Boot the ball and jump the wall,
Run and skip and grow.

When you're old, your toes get cold
And arthritis strikes and gout,
It's easy to use your dancing shoes
When your feet can't skip about.

Rohan Patel
Bickley Park School, Bickley

The Soldier

As a boy he was smiling and bright
His laughter infectious, his eyes alight
A group of friends always with me
Every day so full and free

No one knew the terrible fears
The dark and dread that brought the tears
How could one so blessed by life
Be threatened with bullets, guns and strife?

Sent to lands where one law was rule
Against the peoples the dictator was cruel
The soldier fought what he was told to believe
In freedom, lies and to succeed

Now a tyrant has gone
To face the war crimes that he has done
Everyone knew, everyone said
No one was there, as my friend lay dead.

Gabriel Sherliker (12)
Bickley Park School, Bickley

Aliens

Aliens come from a distant land,
they have three claws on each hand.

Their eyes shine like that of pearls,
I could not tell whether they were boys or girls.

They were so different from us
and were covered in pus.

I managed not to shout,
when one tried to sniff me with its snout.

Then they flew away,
perhaps to come another day.

Michael Wynne-Roberts (12)
Bickley Park School, Bickley

How Green Is Your Environment?

By making sure the goods you buy,
Soaps, detergents or apple pie.

Be organic, recycled or ozone friendly
Or don't you care environmentally?

Cars and trucks bellow smoke,
Enough to make the whole world choke.

Everything is made of plastic,
it never rots and that is drastic.

Collect your papers and save your tins
And put your glass in the correct bins.

Before you drop your junk, think green
And keep our planet nice and clean.

Marc Saunders (13)
Bickley Park School, Bickley

What Is It?

Faster than boarding down the terrain,
Smooth as thoughts in your brain.

It sparkles like a diamond ring
And glows like the sun in the early morning.

A sound as sweet as a hummingbird,
It's so perfect, it's hardly heard.

You can feel the breeze in your face,
Within seconds, the force makes you brace.

Precision, perfection and good engineering,
To have my own is what I am dreaming.

If you can guess what this is,
You may have your own, in a few years.

Duran Remzi (12)
Bickley Park School, Bickley

The Lion

He hides in the bushes,
Quiet and proud,
Watching the deer,
Prancing in the sunshine.

Slowly he creeps,
Studying his prey,
Which way is he going?
Thinks the predator.

Tensing his back legs,
He judges the distance,
Ready to pound,
The deer does not expect a thing.

Then, suddenly,
He fires himself
Right at his lunch,
But the deer has a hunch!

The lion received a face full of dirt,
The deer does not end up getting hurt!

Oliver Judge (12)
Bickley Park School, Bickley

Lost

I got lost today in town
I searched high and low
But I did not know where to go
I searched for my parents in every shop
But ended up buying a top
I kept on searching all through the day
Unfortunately I got lost along the way
I finally found my way back home
To find my parents talking on the phone
I wondered if my parents had noticed
That I had got lost in town today.

Jonathan Poole (12)
Bickley Park School, Bickley

My Fears

My fears wait by my door at night,
when it's dark I long for the light.

When I'm alone, I feel the fear,
I find a friend and keep him near.

When I'm in bed, I fear my fear,
my sweat trickles down like a tear.

In my mind I'm in a cave,
waiting for the light as a wave.

I know the fear follows me,
like a monster chasing me.

In the light, its cover's a shadow,
but when it's dark, it waits at my window.

Even thought I should face it,
I confront it every second of every minute

because it hollers in my ears
and wants me to unleash my fears.

Richard Langridge (12)
Bickley Park School, Bickley

Rugby Must Be Lovely

Rugby must be lovely
When it's all dark and damp

Crowd is cheering loudly
As loud as a 30,000 watt amp

Rugby must be lovely
When it's mucky and raining

Mud is all around us
Mums are getting annoyed with the washing

But what is really lovely in rugby
Is when you win the game.

Ben Stanley (12)
Bickley Park School, Bickley

Dying For Spring

Now's when the coats come out,
because that's what autumn's about.

Magnificent leaves are falling,
angry foxes have been calling.

Green glossy leaves die brown,
then leaves to the compost mound.

Woods with only naked trees,
children with filthy, bruised knees.

Every morning sharp and brisk,
each morning enveloped in mist.

Beneath, crunching at my feet
and rustling on the ground,

Squirrels scavenge for hidden treasure,
big, brown conkers in their shell like leather.

There's only one way this will go away,
we'll have to wait for a spring day.

Charlie Phillips (12)
Bickley Park School, Bickley

The Old Oak Tree

Through the gnarled branches the biting wind whipped
Through the spindly hand of each lifeless branch.
A cloud like a dark sheet then covered the moon
And the forest was plunged into a deadly darkness.

But somehow, as if by some strange, hidden light
The old, dead oak tree stayed illuminated.
The moon came back out and shadows filled the forest
While the waves pounded restlessly against the great cliff.

The full moon now brightly lit up the old oak
As the silhouetted branches swayed in the sea breeze.
Far in the distance a clock tower could be heard
As the oak tree stood there tall, the clock struck midnight.

Karl Wimble (12)
Bickley Park School, Bickley

England

England is a place that has lots of rain
But really it is quite a shame
Of all the beautiful pastures green
Many of which I have never seen

England's armies are very strong
But to use them all would be very wrong
They would blow the other army to Timbuktu
And may lose some soldiers, but only a few

England has a victorious queen
Who really likes to eat ice cream
She wears her crown all day long
With jewels the size of an atom bomb

Overall England is
A place where you would want to live
So much to do, so much to see
There's nowhere else I'd rather be.

Oliver Robinson (12)
Bickley Park School, Bickley

Greed

I am what lurks in each man's heart,
I am what you will find in everyone.

I am what destroys good men,
what causes death among many.

I am what controls desire,
without a care of whom it is.

Good men and bad,
are all as weak.

The unhappy find me more,
for they are not satisfied.

So they call on me,
for I am greed, and can help at any time.

Sam Jackson (12)
Bickley Park School, Bickley

A Full Moon Of Curiosity

Down on my local golf course,
Lives my favourite brown horse,
With a dog and a cow,
Which aren't here right now
As they are up in Leadon.

I laid in my tent,
When I had an intent,
I opened the door
To a horse on the floor,
But this was not my plan.

Oh! I have to do something about it,
Yes! I need to make sure that it's done,
But whenever I need some help,
I definitely know the one!

So I took the reins of the brown horse,
Which tugged my ordanance map,
But it did not fall all alone! No!
It fell with my precious hat.

Nicholas Fryett (10)
Bickley Park School, Bickley

Pancake Madness!

When I hear *sizzle, bang* in the kitchen
I know I've got pancakes for tea
They flip themselves over in the pan
They stay as flat as stingrays in the ocean
The sugar on top is like snow on a mountain
The lemon is like the rain
They spin around on my plate
When I try to get to the biggest bit
When I roll them up they become
Fast trains going into a tunnel
They scream *aaarrrggghhh!*
And then they're gone!

Josie Warner & Amy Bentham (11)
Birkbeck Primary School, Sidcup

Space Poem

I want to be an astronaut,
to travel in my spacesuit
and get around Mars
and look at all the stars.

I'd love to jump on the moon,
like a bouncing prune,
go very fast in my spacecraft
and pick up all the moon dust.

I'd jump along the stars,
race on Mars,
touch all the comets
and use my gamma ray.

Hope I meet an alien,
see if they are green
and hope they are not mean.

James Hoadley (10)
Birkbeck Primary School, Sidcup

Roast Seaside

The broccoli is a tall, long, wavy palm tree giving shade to the plate
The gravy splashes against the potatoes like the furious sea
The swede is bright and yellow like the golden sand
The chicken breasts are boats floating in the gravy
The chicken skin is towels being laid on the plate
My fork stabs against the hard potatoes, which are rocks
The peas bounce up and down as if they are beach balls
                                    being played with
And the runner beans roll about in the sand as if they are people.

Grace Power & Sarah Martin (11)
Birkbeck Primary School, Sidcup

Red Jelly

It wobbles like a penguin
As it slurps onto the plate.
It is as red as a fireball,
When you stick your fork in
It splits like an earthquake.
It tastes lovely when it enters your mouth,
It wobbles in your mouth crazily,
When you sit there lazily.

Ryan Wall & George McMahon (11)
Birkbeck Primary School, Sidcup

Chocolate

The chocolate snaps
Like a twig in a wood
I see its nostrils
Which it breathes through
Its brown skin's wrapped around
Cold and creamy in your mouth
So dreamy and bubbly
It goes down south.

Luke Rayfield (11)
Birkbeck Primary School, Sidcup

I Want To Be An Astronaut

I want to be an astronaut
go to Venus and Mars
and play with all the football stars
play with my best mate
when I train I'm always late.

Charlie Barnard (9)
Birkbeck Primary School, Sidcup

Tests And More Tests

Turn over, now you may begin,
It is not a race, you cannot win.
Tests and more tests is all we do,
It's not fair because I need the loo.
It's not fair Miss, what can I do?
Don't blame me, it's Grace too!
Please tell me what to do.

I think I'm going mad now,
I keep thinking that I'm a boat's sail.
I can see Grace is holding on,
It's obvious that these tests are a big con.
Oh no, it's pencils down,
I feel like a big clown.
I haven't written anything down,
But I've tried so hard, I know I deserve a crown.
Help me Miss, what can I do?
You still haven't helped me and I need the loo!

Becky Weir (10)
Birkbeck Primary School, Sidcup

Venus, Saturn And Mars

I like to look at the stars,
Venus, Saturn and Mars
And if I was an astronaut,
I would really study the stars.

I would like to look at the planets,
Especially the Milky Way,
It looks and tastes so nice,
It would really lead me the way.

I would like to go in a ship
And it would be as small as a pip
And when I get out onto the moon,
I would be joyful as a baboon.

Henry Walker (10)
Birkbeck Primary School, Sidcup

Tests And More Tests

Tests and more tests
They're just like a bunch of nets
They'll all come at once
And I'll be the dunce
Literacy, science and maths
I'm turning into a psychopath
Tests and more tests

The ticking of the clock
Oh my smelly sock!
The test is over
I'm rolling over
The bell is ringing
My head is pinging
Tests, no more tests!

Josef Laklia (10)
Birkbeck Primary School, Sidcup

My Space Poem

I wish I was a spaceman,
I would go and visit Mars,
Probably see some aliens
And look down at some cars.

After, I would go to Pluto,
I hope it's not that cold,
There might even be an ice cone,
I could even hold a stone.

Next, I will go to Venus,
After, I'm off to the moon,
Probably eat some cheese,
Then go back in the afternoon.

Callum McManus-Todd (10)
Birkbeck Primary School, Sidcup

I Was In Space

I wish I could go to space,
Oh what a wonderful place,
You should see my face,
I was in space!

I went to the moon,
I heard a weird boom,
It was only a tune,
I was in space.

I went to Mars,
To see all the stars,
To goes on for yards,
I was in space.

I came home to Earth,
My dad was on the turf
And my brother was playing on the kerb,
I am home!

Alfie Fraser (10)
Birkbeck Primary School, Sidcup

Tests And More Tests

Tests, tests are really bad,
That's why at playtime I'm really glad,
When I'm doing my tests,
I always try to do my best.

When I look up and see the clock,
I always look at my lucky sock.
When I did my maths test,
Loads of times I had to guess!

Emma Matthews (10)
Birkbeck Primary School, Sidcup

Tests And More Tests

The page's over, I'll begin,
These tests have got me in a spin,
I'm stuck within a sea of thought,
I've not done anything, I've been caught!

I'm in all playtime, really bored,
'Oh please save me, save me Lord!'
I'm going mad, I've finished now,
What just hit me? Ow!
I eat my lunch in the hall
And in PE, basketball.

The end of school, finally,
I've bumped into a chestnut tree,
I eat my dinner, go to bed,
The sea of thoughts rushed through my head.

Alex Dane (10)
Birkbeck Primary School, Sidcup

My Dad Is An Astronaut!

My dad is an astronaut,
He soars through the sky,
He says hello to aliens,
When they're passing by.

My dad is an astronaut,
He flies to the moon,
He fills his pockets up with stardust
And comes home very soon.

My dad is an astronaut,
His rocket all glittering gold,
When he comes home, he always brings back
Some moondust for me to hold!

Charmaine Zsigo-Oliver (10)
Birkbeck Primary School, Sidcup

If I Was An Astronaut

If I was an astronaut,
I'd fly to the Milky Way,
I'd go and see some comets
And a gamma ray.

If I was an astronaut,
I would go to tickle stars.
I would fly around for ages
And end up eating Mars.

If I was an astronaut,
I would dig a hole so hollow.
I'll ride a meteor
And end up on Apollo.

If I was an astronaut,
I would go and pick some stardust.
I would fly around the universe
And my ship would be a stick of dust.

Faye O'Callaghan (10)
Birkbeck Primary School, Sidcup

Tests And More Tests

Tests and tests I always do,
That's why I always nip to the loo.
I really hate all the tests,
But my mum says I'm the best.

Maths, English, RE too,
Have we got anymore tests to do?
All the tests we do makes my head ache,
But when I get home I have a milkshake.

Katie Mandy (10)
Birkbeck Primary School, Sidcup

Space Poem

I want to be an astronaut,
to travel in my spacesuit,
pick up lots of stardust
and travel along to Mars
amongst all the stars.

It would be good to go
Very fast in my spacecraft
To see if my brother laughed
I could scoop up all the dust
While I'm jumping on the moon

I could speed along past Venus
To use my gamma ray
Touch all the comets
And fly back past all the stars
Landing firmly when back to Mars.

Jessica Smith (10)
Birkbeck Primary School, Sidcup

Tests And More Tests

Tests and tests I really hate
That is why I'm always late
Maths and English, science too
History I like to do!

So when I go out to play
I really enjoy the sunny day
Then when the bell goes, I'm really sad
To do those tests that are really bad.

Annie MaCarthy (10)
Birkbeck Primary School, Sidcup

My Cat Went To Spain

My cat went to Spain in an aeroplane
He spread the rain around the footie game
When the players were sad
They were pretty mad
The cat jumped through the flame
To win the footie game
When he got home
He went to the Millennium Dome
Where he broke the big body and went to jail
When he got out he said
'Wow!'

He went on a roller coaster
And broke his back
Sooner or later he was
On a *rack!*

Katie McNally (9)
Birkbeck Primary School, Sidcup

Seaside Scene

I see the sea sparkling like a star, splashing
Calmly onto the rough rocks.

I hear the screeching seagulls, soaring, gliding,
Swooping, circling in the clear cloudless sky.

I smell the salty seaweed, dark green like leaves,
Floating and slithering in the gentle waves.

I touch the hot, smooth sand as it sprinkles
Through my fingers and toes.

I feel calm and sleepy as I relax
In the warm summer sun.

Zoe Bromfield (10)
Birkbeck Primary School, Sidcup

Space, The Final Frontier

Space, the final frontier
And don't forget I hate beer
I would fly to space and land on the moon
And help them defeat the Looney Toons
I will invite Callum and Alfie to a party
Don't forget to invite Captain Pasckarky

Now this is my life in space oh yeah
I just remembered to pack my suitcase.

Michael Waring (9)
Birkbeck Primary School, Sidcup

Rockets And Stars

Rockets, rockets, in the air,
Rockets, rockets, everywhere.
Rockets, rockets, can always fly,
Rockets, rockets, in the sky.

Stars, stars, float around,
Stars, stars, don't touch the ground.

Everything, everywhere,
Everything is in the air.

Daniel Bryan (10)
Birkbeck Primary School, Sidcup

Exploding Fireworks

Popping candy dances on your tongue
Popping candy is a rainbow cut into bite-size pieces
Popping candy is an exploding firework in your mouth
Popping candy is like shards of glass stabbing your tongue.

Sara Newark & Emily Greenyer (11)
Birkbeck Primary School, Sidcup

Sea

Peacefully drifting silently,
Shimmering ripples gleaming,
Twinkling like stars,
As it slithers down slowly.

Skimming over rocks,
Whipping spray into the air.
Hammering down loudly,
Tumbling, dashing, zooming.

Flowing calmly,
Gentle ripples as the sunset reflects.
Calm, shimmering, swaying slowly,
Drifting quietly.

Samantha Roper (10)
Birkbeck Primary School, Sidcup

Water Poem

Slithering slowly, silently,
Twinkling ripples, sparkle and shimmer,
Gliding gently.

Darting down
And whipping up spray,
Crashing and hammering
Onto rocks,
Noisily falling

Gentle ripples shimmering, swaying,
Calmly drifting down with the current,
Fish swimming.

Hannah Johnston (10)
Birkbeck Primary School, Sidcup

I Want To Be A Spaceman

I want to be a spaceman,
Fly away to Mars,
See the craters on the moon
And all the flashing stars!

See the ring round Saturn
And the gases on Venus,
Travel round the Milky Way
And watch my helmet float away.

Daniel Tooher (10)
Birkbeck Primary School, Sidcup

Waterfalls

Slithering, sliding, shining peacefully,
gliding, gleaming, shimmering sleepily.

Clashing, crashing, bashing loudly,
falling, zooming, darting quickly.

Shimmering, swirling, whirling softly,
flowing, glowing, going slowly.

Matthew Rogers (10)
Birkbeck Primary School, Sidcup

Invading The Worms' Lair

Light brown worms sleeping on my plate,
tempting me to enter their home,
the worms try to wriggle their way free
but still enter the dark tunnel of doom!

Pembe Mustafa & Aarron Feeney (11)
Birkbeck Primary School, Sidcup

Space

I just got in a rocket,
I couldn't go anywhere,
I thought there'd be a socket,
Under my rocket chair.

I thought I'd seen an alien,
It was friendly, sad, vain,
I hope its name is Damian,
I bet I arrive in Spain.

I wish I could see some stars,
While landing upon Mars.
I can speed through the Milky Way,
Using my gamma ray.

Elliott Smither (10)
Birkbeck Primary School, Sidcup

Water Drop!

Swaying softly,
Gliding down quickly,
Quietly, there it goes.

Clashing, crashing,
Dashing down,
Shooting, skimming,
Over rough rocks.

Flapping tails of fishes in the lake,
Sunset shining and reflecting on the peaceful water,
Whirling, twirling everywhere.

Sabiha Mahmut (10)
Birkbeck Primary School, Sidcup

Frog

Bouncing and hopping,
Lily pad to lily pad,
Bounce! Hop! Hop! Bounce!
I wonder where it's going.
Onto the bank,
Through leaves,
Over twigs,
Bounce!

Bouncing and hopping,
Lily pad to lily pad.
Bounce! Hop! Hop! Bounce!
I wonder where it's going.
Over twigs,
Through leaves,
Onto the bank,

1 . . . 2 . . . 3 . . . 4 . . . 5 . . .
Splash!

Georgina Pollock (10)
Birkbeck Primary School, Sidcup

I Want To Be An Astronaut

I want to be an astronaut
go to Venus and to Mars
and every day I would play football with the stars
and every time I score a goal the aliens will go, 'Raa!'
I would drive a car and sit on a star
I'd go along saying whooo!
Can you imagine it?
I can too
But the only thing I'm doing today
is eating my tea and going out to play.

Charlie Lawrence (10)
Birkbeck Primary School, Sidcup

Care For The World

Don't waste paper, don't be mean,
Keep the world nice and clean.
Trees are important, they help us breathe,
Don't waste paper, don't cut trees!
Cars are whizzing, leaving smoke,
Don't let the children cough and choke.
Save for the future, keep your motivation,
Hopefully we will have more conservation.
Look after the environment for us all,
We will have clean air more and more.
Rake away the rubbish, rake and rake,
Care for the ponds, care for the lakes.
We don't want dirty air, don't assume,
It won't clean itself, just smell the fumes!
Dirty air is flowing here and there,
Nobody seems to care.
Keep the world tidy, keep the world clean,
We don't want to hear you scream.

Muhammed Patel (10)
Cleves Primary School, London

Love The Environment

Look after the world,
Make it well,
It's like a shell.

It's a place to live,
It can also give.

Think of the trees
Without their leaves,
Our world should be free
From disease.

Hina Mahmood (10)
Cleves Primary School, London

Fireworks

They are sparkly, they are fiery,
Can be dangerous too,
They are colourful, loud,
Exciting!
They are flames of sky,
I feel happy and excited when I see them,
Fireworks, *fireworks*,
Makes me always think of stars.

Nadia Hamid (11)
Cleves Primary School, London

Kitten

She's soft, tabby and ginger,
A mini tiger, a small lioness,
I feel like her mother,
I feel important, full of care and love,
When I watch her sleeping.

Keimara Thomas (10)
Cleves Primary School, London

Snow

Soft, smooth and cold,
Silky and white,
Like mini clouds floating in the sky,
Like a cold sheet,
I wish it would fall forever.

Tania Denis (10)
Cleves Primary School, London

Friendship

As strong as a bond between two hearts
Joining like the sun and moon
Like generations passing by -
Too soon.

Everyone needs a friend
A very special friend
To help you when you are down
To help you mend

A soulless body
Without a heart
Needs a friend
Right from the start

They'll be there to cheer you up
When you're feeling sad
And they'll be there to calm you down
When you're feeling mad

Without a friend you're nothing
You just need them so
Breaking friendships is a sin
And to Heaven you may not go.

Salma Begum (10)
Cleves Primary School, London

You're My Friend

You're my friend 'til the day I die.
The day I lose you, I'll cry and cry.
You're an angel that was sent to me,
You're caught in my heart.
You set me free.

Charmaine Sinclair-Ssekandi (11)
Cleves Primary School, London

My Puppy

She is so beautiful, soft and fun.
She's so great, I show her to everyone.
She is cute with her furry lip,
She gives me a close friendship.
She can run at supersonic speed,
With a soft, fluffy tail.
She is always there for me,
So I will never fail.
We play 'all posh' sometimes
And she'll sip.
This is her and our friendship.
She's a great friend to me,
Like a close sister.
She's with me all day.
I don't have to miss her.
We play lots of games.
She tumbles like a battleship.
This is her and my close friendship.

Mikka Brown (10)
Cleves Primary School, London

My Football

Football -
Round, leathery, smooth.
Like a spinning moon,
A sun
To be played with,
Until
It falls
Over the fence.

Amjad Mumtaz Khan (10)
Cleves Primary School, London

Give/Care

Give
Give money to the poor
They have a right like us
Give food to the birds
In the sky, above
Give love to the world
Keep it clean
It'll give you back
Love, you know what I mean?

Care
Some people don't care
But I do, all about nature
So honest and true
If I could care for it all
I'd do that, care for all
The life in the world.

Solomon Khan (10)
Cleves Primary School, London

I Had A Dream

I've just had a dream
This is how it goes
It flows and flows

Birds in the sky
Pure and clean
So you know what I mean
Skies so fresh
Clean as the birds
People with it
Walking free
A dream so clean
People walking free
People who care.

Hassan Ishfaq (10)
Cleves Primary School, London

Friends

She is caring as a mother bird
She is as trustworthy as the spring
She is as sharing as a computer
Honest as a bird
Respectful as a teacher
She is a funny and kind friend
Fabulous as a butterfly
And as kind as a kitten
She is friendly as a monkey
Gentle as a soft ball
Supportive as a mouse
She is polite as my mother.

Habiba Khatun (10)
Cleves Primary School, London

Friends

Friends make you feel safe and warm,
They'll hold you safely through a storm
A friend will forever be your guide
No matter what, they'll be on your side.

People who are friends will always care
When you're in trouble they will be there
I've got friends who like me see!
That's how friends should always be.

Amanda Nnakku (11)
Cleves Primary School, London

Planes

Quick, fast as fire!
The best things, made to last,
They get there in a flash!
Above you,
You know what they can do.

Soni Baja (10)
Cleves Primary School, London

Friends And Family

They are so kind,
They're always with me, on my mind,
Caring, loving all the time -
I wonder sometimes if they're mine.

I could not live without my friends,
A day without them would not end,
They help me and I help them too -
We're best friends and that's so true.

My family sometimes drive me mad,
But really, honestly make me glad.
Helping smiling every day,
But wow! Come on, they're never sad.

Friends and family are here to care,
Always mine when I say a prayer.

Gabrielle Bratton (11)
Cleves Primary School, London

Fireworks

Beautiful but dangerous -
Like the sea,
Like splodges of glitter
They make me want to explode
With glee,
Sometimes I feel wobbly inside,
Like jelly,
Fireworks!
Fireworks!
Fireworks!
Make me think of falling glitter,
Splodges in the sky,
Yeah!

Nazmin Begum (11)
Cleves Primary School, London

The Speedy Train

Trains are fast
Quick, speedy, enormous
Snakes moving along
Like boats whizzing
Sometimes creeping slowly.

A tortoise sometimes walking
A speedy train
Makes me feel relaxed
I'll be there in a flash or two.

Mahfujur Rahman (10)
Cleves Primary School, London

My Friend, Kamrul

As fabulous as a box of fireworks
As helpful as a winter squirrel
As sensible as a jar of yellow honey
As funny as a falling clown
As quiet as a sleeping mouse
As clumsy as an old goat!
He claps like an echo in a tunnel
He is Kamrul.

Michael Ortega (10)
Cleves Primary School, London

Anhurul

Makes me laugh
Wicked as a magician
Fun as a snooker ball
He's wild as a monkey
Thinks like a dolphin
He plays like a cat
Fights playfully like my dog
He is *great!*

Anderson Lizano (11)
Cleves Primary School, London

Our Friend, Aaron

He is funny
He makes us laugh!
He never lets us down
He is as funny as a comedian
He makes us laugh like monkeys
He always tries his hardest
He is the next '2-Pac'!
He is a friend
A best friend
He is just Aaron.

Hassan Ishfaq (9) & Soloman Khan (10)
Cleves Primary School, London

Pollution

Let's look for a solution
For all this pollution

Keep litter off the floor
We can't stand it anymore!

Think of the future of us kids
Always keeps on your dustbin lids!

Think of the waste which goes in the sea
Clean it up for you and me.

Khaleel Abdi (11)
Cleves Primary School, London

Nature

N ature is beautiful
A re you a person who likes nature?
T rue nature hovers through the air
U nder the trees lies more nature
R ain helps a lot of natural processes
E verything has a bit of nature in it.

Nahid Hasan Karim (8)
Cleves Primary School, London

Bart Simpson

A funny joker
A smart, cool boy
Calculator clever
A fun, playful dog
Helpful as a sister
A kind genius
Great as a pop star
Friendly as the world
Respectful as an animal
Skateboards like the wind
Happy with his money
Jokes like a jester
Good sport with pals
A superb, super man
Positive as a gold sticker
My mate, Bart.

Hamza Jilani (10)
Cleves Primary School, London

Flowers!

Lovely trees,
The good part of nature,
Beautiful, peaceful, brings no harm,
It brings you views,
With lovely news,
Makes you feel so happy,
Joyful, cheerful and funny,
Birds singing,
People cheering and relaxing,
Beautiful like the roses shining,
It brings the weather
And all humans back together.

Priyanthan Sriharon (9)
Cleves Primary School, London

Season Song

In spring the flowers start to grow
And the sun starts to shine
Animals come out of hibernation
Which makes me feel fine!

In summer, it's very hot
When everyone goes to play
Holidays for everyone
On a very hot day

In autumn the leaves on the trees fall off
And it starts to get cold
The raindrops start to fall
And summer starts to fold

In winter it gets colder
And it starts to snow
People build snowmen
Ten in a row.

Sanisha Jani (9)
Cleves Primary School, London

Nature

Learning about nature is fun,
Animals are fun but sometimes you have to run!
When you go to the forest with friends,
There can be sometimes pathway bends.
Where butterflies and birds fly around,
And most of the time you don't hear a sound.
Waterfalls, monkeys and trees,
Don't all need leaves.
And that's a bit about nature my friend,
And this is how this story ends.

Sultana Hussain (9)
Cleves Primary School, London

Friends, Friends Everywhere!

Friends are here
Friends are there
Friends, friends everywhere!

Some are short
Some are tall
Friends, friends everywhere . . .

Friends are coming,
I can't wait
Friends, friends celebrate!

We're going to McDonald's
Have our meal

Friends, friends
Make me feel

Special!

Aisha Umar (10)
Cleves Primary School, London

Our Environment

Keep the air bright and clean
Breathe it, feel it, don't be mean

Throw your litter in the bin
Recycle waste, it'll make you grin

Clean your rubbish off our street
Keep our gardens smelling sweet

Cut down your bills, save on fuel
Keep fish alive, don't be cruel

Look after it, it'll care for you
The environment has a heart that's true.

Rose Kahya (10)
Cleves Primary School, London

The Streets

I am a king
When I walk down my street
My heart starts to beat as I walk
Down my street
There's danger everywhere
(That's something I can't bear)
On my street
Where I hear my beat
When the sun's gone down
The stars come up
I leave my street
I've found my door
Here's my stop
The noises continue all around
Lots of different sounds
I'm safe home now
Can you hear the beat of my street?

Jamie Patterson (9)
Cleves Primary School, London

Friends

F riends are funny, fine and kind
R eally fine, they always shine!
I f you have them let them know;
   they'll be there 'til the end.
E very friend you meet and find
   will always learn that to be kind means
N ever letting go.
D id you know you should open your eyes
   to friends.
S ome friends are nice, some are mean,
   always pick the one you need.

Reece Larwood (9)
Cleves Primary School, London

Our Friend, Saeedah

She's a fun fox
A kind rabbit
As bright as the sun
Happy as the moon
As funny as a banana
Colourful like a rainbow
As clever as a monkey
Saeedah, playful as a kitten
Saeedah, smiles like a butterfly
Laughing like a hyena.

Nadia Hamid (10) & Nazmin Begum (10)
Cleves Primary School, London

My Friend, Trevor

He comes to me when I am lonely,
Reading books makes him as happy as summertime,
He makes me laugh as loud as an elephant,
His smile is as big as Africa,
He listens to me when I need him to,
His lifetime superstar is James Bond,
When he sees Mum he runs like a cheetah,
He loves everyone,
He is the sun.

Omar Awad (10)
Cleves Primary School, London

Huda

She is kind as a nurse
She is like a yellow bulb
She has a good heart
Helps me when I'm stuck
Huda is quiet and calm
She is like the sea.

Tahira Zahid (10)
Cleves Primary School, London

Friendship Is A Key

It never ends,
Remember it spreads around the world,
Try not to lose it,
Even when the world goes round,
We don't lose each other,
We are friends forever,
With one another,
Never take it away from me,
I don't want it to be broken,
Lots of memories are in my mind,
From the past to the present.

Jannat Musaizi (8)
Cleves Primary School, London

The Witches' Spell

Dancing round the cauldron now,
The smell of poison, horrific but how?
The toad will watch without being known,
From underneath its secret stone.
Sleeping is a different slot,
Giving away your first born tot.
Double, double, toil and trouble,
Fire burn and cauldron bubble.

A lizard's brain, with a hint of rain,
Add together nightmares and pain.
A tiger's claw and a puppy's paw,
Boiled and grilled on the graveyard floor.
Rat's eye and a horse's hoof,
Mixed together with a large shark's tooth.
Beetles and spiders stirred in the pot,
Add a bull's horn and that's the lot!
Double, double, toil and trouble,
Fire burn and cauldron bubble.

Andrew Mack (10)
Cookham Rise Primary School, Maidenhead

The Witches' Spell

Around the cauldron we go
We put in poisoned guts
A toad, from under a stone
For 31 days and nights
Poisoned at night
You do this first
Double, double, toil and trouble
Fire burn and cauldron bubble
Body of slug very runny
Pencil lead and a rubber
Eye of newt, tongue of a cat
A bee's heart and a deer's antler
A bird's wing and a tongue of a baby
The tail of a horse and mud off the ground
A human's liver and kidneys dipped in poison
Double, double, toil and trouble
Fire burn and cauldron bubble
Skin of a frog and tooth of a dragon
A dinosaur's bone and a lung of a whale
Skeleton of a shark and nose of a dolphin
A voice box and a lion's mane
You need this to complete the spell
Double, double, toil and trouble
Fire burn and cauldron bubble.

Naomi Rawlinson (11)
Cookham Rise Primary School, Maidenhead

The Witches' Spell

Round and round the witches go
Round the cauldron through rain and snow
Chanting, singing all day long
But still the cauldron stands strong
Tongue of a newt and a fish's eye
Brain of a cat and an old mince pie
Double, double, toil and trouble
Fire burn and cauldron bubble
A live beetle in an old smelly sock
Fin of a shark and a little black frock
Leaf of the tree on the tallest mountain
Green murky water from the witches' fountain
A little black cloud caught from above
Tail from a rabbit and wing of a dove
Double, double, toil and trouble
Fire burn and cauldron bubble
Stripes of a zebra, tail of a dog
Scales of a crocodile and snout of a hog
Shell of a snail and fangs of a bat
A lion's mane and tail of a rat
Black bear's fur for a windy day
Keeps them going all the way
Double, double, toil and trouble
Fire burn and cauldron bubble!

Rebecca Curley (10)
Cookham Rise Primary School, Maidenhead

The Witches' Spell

Round and round the cauldron we're walking,
Saying spells as we're talking.
Then we throw in almighty things,
Like cats' tongues and bats' wings.
Burning cauldron show your light,
Give some people lots of fright.
Double, double, burn and bubble,
Tell Macbeth to make trouble.
Put in a pinch of rhino's horn,
That should make some people mourn.
Take a rattle from a snake,
Add it to a boiled hake.
Then you add a lady's nose,
That will make a door close.
Double, double, burn and bubble,
Tell Macbeth to make trouble.
Throw in three children now,
Then you get a brain from a cow,
Add a shell of a winkle,
That will make your fingers wrinkle.
Mush it into scolding tea,
That's your potion, can't you see?
Double, double, burn and bubble,
Tell Macbeth to make trouble!

Arif Suleiman (10)
Cookham Rise Primary School, Maidenhead

A Witch's Spell

I beg you please from me to you,
Release, release a storm is due;
Bubbling cauldron of blood does sizzle,
Long claw nails filed with a chisel;
Double, double, toil and trouble,
Fire burn and cauldron bubble.
Hear the cries of the bony black cats,
Rubbery tails and slimy guts from wild fat rats;
Round three times on my spellbound broom,
For this frog's leg shall shrivel too soon;
Double, double, toil and trouble,
Fire burn and cauldron bubble.
Misty, cold and winter weather,
Drop from chicken's leg a tasselled feather;
Wound and bent is the bloodstained steel,
Stabbed by the fang of an electric eel;
Double, double, toil and trouble,
Fire burn and cauldron bubble.
Grey knotted hair all greasy and old,
A packed lunch sandwich covered in mould;
Big slimy eyeballs filed with cheese,
Unfortunately, served with crushed mushy peas;
Double, double, toil and trouble,
Fire burn and cauldron bubble.

Sofia Gladki (10)
Cookham Rise Primary School, Maidenhead

The Witches' Spell

Round the cauldron we shall go,
In goes the ingredients we throw,
Eye of newt, ear of bat,
Leg of frog, tail of rat,
Tooth of bear, bone of dog,
Beak of duck, bark of log.

Double, double, toil and trouble,
This will make your belly bubble.

Fin of fish, wing of fly,
Petal of flower, with a dead dog's eye,
Mix it fast and mix it quick,
One smell of it will make you sick.

Double, double, toil and trouble,
This will make your belly bubble.

Nose of trout, sting of nettle,
This will keep you fettle,
Tail of lizard, a monkey's yell,
This is worse than the demons from Hell.

Double, double, toil and trouble,
This will make your belly bubble.

Laura Tull (10)
Cookham Rise Primary School, Maidenhead

The Three Witches' Poem

Fire burn, rain drop,
Stir the pot and plan a plot,
Boil and bake in the cauldron goes . . .

A brown log
And a black dog.

Bee's sting,
Dragon wing.

Bling bling,
Ting ting.

We will be king,
King, king, king.

Fire burn, rain drop,
Stir the pot and plan a plot,
Boil and bake in the cauldron goes . . .

More and more,
Here it goes,
Fox's eyeballs,
One man,
Two metal cans.

Jake Walker (10)
Cookham Rise Primary School, Maidenhead

The Witches' Spell

Round and round the stew pot now,
Pour in guts of poisoned cow,
Fish that coward in the reeds,
Today's the day we do deeds,
Slugs and snails from under rocks,
Legs and limbs from rotting ox.

Bubble, bubble, toil and trouble,
Sizzling hearts and stew pot double.

Hind legs of some puppy dogs,
Squished between decaying logs,
Leg of horse and heart of goat,
Eye of mouse and lung of stoat,
Piglet's snout and magpie's tail,
Mouldy fruit and a fingernail.

For a spell of a shameful life,
Like an edge of a jagged knife.

Bubble, bubble, boil with trouble,
Sizzling hearts and stew pot double.

Fur of skunk, ears of moles,
Mummies come with fractured skull,
Live in tombs, come from cases,
Claw of rat, dying races,
Put in smells and fumes of rot,
For these are substances for our stew pot.

Bubble, bubble, boil with trouble,
Sizzling hearts and stew pot double.

Zoe Tolley (10)
Cookham Rise Primary School, Maidenhead

The Witches' Spell

As we three witches stir the pot,
We're not running but we like to plot.
Throw in the pot a cold rat's tail
And the hair of a lion's mane.
For nights and days we've worked for this,
So put in a toad that got a kiss.
Double, double, toil and trouble,
Fire burn and cauldron bubble.
Add a slice of a human's nose
And the wings of some feathered crows.
Nose of a dog, beak of a pigeon,
But only just a little smidgeon!
Pig's tail curling round and round,
An elephant's ear that can't hear a sound.
Add a bit of the sea so cold,
This soup is getting stale and old.
Double, double, toil and trouble,
Fire burn and cauldron bubble.
Add ten scales of a rainbowfish,
We always grant everyone's wish.
Add a PC and all its brains,
A PlayStation lead and all its games.
A mobile phone, sim card too,
Then an owl but just its tu-whit tu-whoo.
Around the oven we sing and dance,
To turn our victims into a trance.
For our troubles, plenty dosh we get,
But beware, watch out for your pet!
Double, double, toil and trouble,
Fire burn and cauldron bubble!

Jessica Pleace (10)
Cookham Rise Primary School, Maidenhead

The Witches' Spell

Bubble, bubble, this spell is trouble,
It will put you in a muddle.
Peas gone rotten,
All things forgotten.
Jelly of cat's eyes,
All covered with flies.
Stir it up, mix it well,
You will have a powerful spell.
Hairs of a shaggy dog,
A tooth of a fat warthog.
Bubble, bubble, this spell is trouble,
It will put you in a muddle.
Pizza all rotten and covered in mould,
Smelly cheese 10 days old.
Fluff from an old man's sock,
Gone all stiff and hard as a rock.
A fluffy feather from a parrot,
Orange and green like an old carrot.
Slime of a snail all gooey and runny,
All the witches find it rather funny.
Bubble, bubble, this spell is trouble,
It will put you in a muddle.
Lollipops all sticky and hairy
And last year's toenails from Auntie Mary.
The smell of Grandad's old shoe,
It smells just like my grandad too.
The green of snot
And horrible grot.
Stir it up and make it thick,
It will surely make you *sick!*

Rebecca Brayne (11)
Cookham Rise Primary School, Maidenhead

A Modern Version Of The Witches' Spell

Double, double, toil and trouble,
Fire burn and cauldron bubble.
In this cauldron there will be,
Some funny things you've never seen,
Like frogs' legs, bat hair, rabbit hair too
And hypnotised monkeys that play the kazoo.
Double, double, toil and trouble,
Fire burn and cauldron bubble.
At last we've nearly finished the spell,
But all we need now is water from the well.
Abracadabra giddily wham,
Get the water as fast as you can!
Double, double, toil and trouble,
Fire burn and cauldron bubble.
Here at last the water stands,
Now dance round the cauldron,
Hand in hand.
Double, double, toil and trouble,
Fire burn and cauldron bubble.

Jodie Macfarren (10)
Cookham Rise Primary School, Maidenhead

The Witches' Spell

Round and round the cook pot go
In goes the poison with a throw
Just add a leg of a frog
And add the hair of a dog
Double, double, toil and trouble
Fire burn and cauldron bubble
Add an insect that is dead
Make sure it has got a head
Just add a smashed plate
Don't ever be late
Double, double, toil and trouble
Fire burn and cauldron bubble.

Shannen Behan (10)
Cookham Rise Primary School, Maidenhead

The Modern Version Of The Witches' Spell

In go the rattlesnakes' tails
In go the elephants' toenails
A squeak of a mouse
Runs in its house
As we turn the stick in the giant pot
They scream to come out
Double, double, toil and trouble
Fire burn and cauldron bubble
An eye of a bat
A wing of a gnat
A slowworm's bloodstained heart
Boom, boom, boom, you can still hear it beating
A salty tooth from a shark
Glow-worms glowing in the midsummer night, it's dark
Double, double, toil and trouble
Fire burn and cauldron bubble.

Charlotte Boulton (10)
Cookham Rise Primary School, Maidenhead

The Witches' Spell

Double, double, toil and trouble,
Fire burn and cauldron bubble.

In the pot amongst the frogs' legs,
Rotten bugs hanging on clothes pegs.
Mouldy grapefruit, shrivelled-up skin,
Anything horrid, lob it in.

Double, double, toil and trouble,
Fire burn and cauldron bubble.

Eyes from lizards, great white shark fins,
Seasoned with a tin of sharp pins.
Gruesome mummies, zombies and rats,
Legs from ants and vampire bats.

Double, double, toil and trouble,
Fire burn and cauldron bubble.

Joe Difford (10)
Cookham Rise Primary School, Maidenhead

The Witches' Spell

Gooey, gooey, watch it glow
Mashed up pieces of pets you know
Eyeballs of a runaway dog
The tongue of a dying hog
Horns of a wounded goat
Tail of a scurrying stoat
The fangs of a vampire bat
The wings of a biting gnat
Gooey, gooey, watch it glow
Mashed up pieces of pets you know
Our mixture will make you weak
Our mixture will make you reek
The froth of our cauldron, blue, yellow and red
The taste of skin that a lizard has shed
Mix it up, you'll get a surprise
The smell is so strong it'll attract a million flies
Gooey, gooey watch it glow
Mashed up pieces of pets you know.

Emma Clark (10)
Cookham Rise Primary School, Maidenhead

The Witches' Spell

Double, double, toil and trouble
Make it burst and make it bubble
Come on witches let's make it scrumble
Toil and trouble
Witches are green and cats are so clean

Double, double, toil and trouble
Come on witches let's make some more trouble
Come on witches let's make a poison

Double, double, toil and trouble
Make it funny and make a bunny.

Sharmaine Hughes (10)
Cookham Rise Primary School, Maidenhead

Witches' Chant

Round about the cauldron go
Humans' eyeballs we all throw
Poison ivy from the garden
Burpy, burpy, beg your pardon
Skulls bubbling on the top
A splash, a splutter and it goes pop

Double, double, toil and trouble
Fire burn and cauldron bubble

Elephant's ear, monkey's toes
Rhino's horn and a cat's nose
Scales of a fish, a dog's brain
Neck of a giraffe and a lion's mane
Tooth of a shark, rotten skin
Horse's tail and a dolphin's fin

Double, double, toil and trouble
Fire burn and cauldron bubble.

Danielle Rickard (10)
Cookham Rise Primary School, Maidenhead

The Witches' Spell

Dancing around the cauldron we go
Throw in some eyes
Nice and slow
A tail of a mouse
Claw of a cat
Mixing nicely round and round
Double, double, toil and trouble
Fire burn, cauldron bubble
Gut of a pig
Wings of a bat
Liver of a rat
Mixing nicely round and round
Double, double, toil and trouble
Fire burn, cauldron bubble.

Rosie Wallis (10)
Cookham Rise Primary School, Maidenhead

The Witches' Spell

In the cauldron the witches throw
Puppy dog tails and also a toe
Eye of cat, fur of mouse
Take the tortoise from out of his house
Double, double, toil and trouble
Fire burn and cauldron bubble
A carrot and potato from the soil
In the cauldron things will boil
Tail of horse and skin of frog
Baby's hair and mud of bog
Double, double, toil and trouble
Fire burn and cauldron bubble
Witches' warts and a spider's leg
A tot of whisky and beer from a keg
In the witches' eyes there's a glimmer
In the cauldron things will simmer
Double, double, toil and trouble
Fire burn and cauldron bubble.

Samantha Dance (10)
Cookham Rise Primary School, Maidenhead

The Witches' Spell

Men's bloody scars
And alien heads from Mars
Octopus tentacles
Snot hanging down like icicles
Rabbit claws
Pussy cat paws
Mixed together with a bucket of sick
Old men's beards
And all things weird
That is what is in my pot
So witches from Saturn's Hell
Make a spell, and make it well.

Ryan Henry (10)
Cookham Rise Primary School, Maidenhead

Witches' Spell

Round and round the witches go
Walking, walking very slow
Brain of a bear
Ear of hare
Double, double, toil and trouble
Fire burn and cauldron bubble
Lion's tooth sharp as a rock
Put in claws of a croc
Giraffe's neck
And a parrot's peck
Double, double, toil and trouble
Fire burn and cauldron bubble
Stir, stir, stir it all up
Don't forget the eyes in the cup
Tongue of a frog
Nose of a hog
These are the ingredients of our spell
Now we must go back down to Hell.

Daniel John (10)
Cookham Rise Primary School, Maidenhead

The Witches' Spell

Double, double, toil and trouble
Fire burn and cauldron bubble

To start our scheme we also need
The shell of a snail
A puppy dog's spleen
The wings of a bat
The eye of a fiend
Venom of snake
Smell of doom
This potion we mix by the light of the moon

Double, double, toil and trouble
Fire burn and cauldron bubble.

Philip Hellmuth (10)
Cookham Rise Primary School, Maidenhead

A Witch's Spell

Round the cauldron we all go,
Into the pot what shall we throw?
The eyes of a sheep, the tail of a dog
And anything else we can find in the fog.
The rattle of a snake and a newly-baked cake,
Put them together and give them a shake.

Double, double, toil and trouble,
Fire burn and cauldron bubble.

Kangaroo's pouch and an elephant's tusk,
Let's catch a bat that comes out at dusk,
We'll stir them all up and add some mud
And then we shall find some animal's blood.
Add a lion's mane and a giraffe's leg
And then we'll feed it to Mystic Meg.

Double, double, toil and trouble,
Fire burn and cauldron bubble.

Ben Wolfe (10)
Cookham Rise Primary School, Maidenhead

Witches' Spell

Double, double, toil and trouble,
Fire burning, the cauldron bubble.
Muddle, bubble, toil and trouble,
Something's about to burst its bubble.
Eye of newt, ear of a bat,
We cook 'em all till they turn a crispy black.
Frog's eyes and a bee with a sting,
We put it all in to make it win.
A bird's wing and pig's skin,
We need it all to make our spell win.
We mix it together to make our brew,
Hopefully the results will be good too.
Double, double, toil and trouble,
Fire burning and cauldron bubble.

Daimion Smith (10)
Cookham Rise Primary School, Maidenhead

The Witches' Spell

Double, double, toil and trouble
Fire burn and cauldron bubble
Double, double, toil and trouble
Fire burn and cauldron bubble
Wigging of a green snake
In the cooker boil and bake
Eye of owl and head of frog
Wings of bat and paw of dog
Sharp's fork and bloodworm's sting
Rat's leg and baby owl's wing
For a charm of powerful trouble
Like a Hell full of witches, boil and bubble
Double, double, toil and trouble
Fire burn and cauldron bubble
Double, double, toil and trouble
Fire burn and cauldron bubble.

Zoe Sharp (10)
Cookham Rise Primary School, Maidenhead

The Witches' Spell

Double, double, toil and trouble,
Fire burn and cauldron bubble.

A tiny strip of horse's hair
And a paw of a big brown bear.

In the cauldron to boil and brew,
Add a nail of a tiny shrew.

Two drops of a baby's tear,
To make the potion smell of fear.

At last we add an eye of a dog
And a leg of a frog.

Double, double, toil and trouble,
Fire burn and cauldron bubble.

Kane Rose (10)
Cookham Rise Primary School, Maidenhead

The Witches' Spell

A chameleon's tongue, a rodent's tooth,
A bird's wing, a horse's hoof,
An ogre's spit, a rat's tail,
A human's eye, the slime of a snail.

Double, double, toil and trouble,
Fire burn and cauldron bubble.

A scale of a fish, lava from a volcano,
A dragon's breath, a cat's eye glow,
Runner's sweat, bee's sting,
A pigeon without a wing.

Double, double, toil and trouble,
Fire burn and cauldron bubble.

A howl of a ghost,
There are some more ingredients, but I've got most,
The heckle of a hag, the snort of a man very old,
Now you know the spell which we have told.

Double, double, toil and trouble,
Fire burn and cauldron bubble.

Clara Millar (10)
Cookham Rise Primary School, Maidenhead

The Lady Of The Ocean

Her hair is as wavy as the Atlantic.
Her eyes are as deep as the ocean.
When her eyes open all of the sea obeys her.
As her body crashes against the shimmering rocks,
The sun shines on her pearl necklace.

As she looks down her slimming body
All she can see is mermen bowing at her side.
As she rolls into the sea she whispers sweet wonders into your mind.
As she slowly strolls into the seven seas,
She inspires every mortal with her flying colours.

Chloe Humphrey (10)
Culverstone Green CP School, Gravesend

Icicle Mountain

The hair looks like a pointed glassy icicle
On top of the ice-cold mountain.
The two blue eyes gazing into the bitterly cold frost.
The lips are as pale as the twisting bitter artic air.
These hands are like frozen icicles in the frosty, cold, frozen mountain.
The arms glistening in the sunlight while the sun goes down.
The knees are as stiff as a frozen mountain.
Two feet glistening in the snow on an ice-cold blanket.

Steven Wincott (10)
Culverstone Green CP School, Gravesend

Winter Man

His hair is so spiky like icicles in a cave.
His eyes are as white as snow.
As the wind blew at him, his cheeks became dark red.
Two blankets of snow on his shoulders.

His fingers are as long as icicles.
His legs are so stiff he can barely walk.
He blows across like a snowstorm.
His laces so cold they are so stiff.

Shane Brown (10)
Culverstone Green CP School, Gravesend

Snow

His shoes are like ice skates on the icy lake.
His legs long like icicles hanging off the house.
The boy's body as cold as the water in the lake in the park.
His fingernails pointy like the tips of icicles falling off trees.
His trousers and T-shirt are white like the snow.
His hair is spiky like icicles.
The boy's eyes like white snowballs.

Samuel Stevens (10)
Culverstone Green CP School, Gravesend

The Lady Of The Ocean

Her hair as wavy as the ocean's tide,
Her skin as pale as the sandy seabed,
The eyes of the bluest and deepest ocean
Glistening like a washed-up pearl,
She has a heart of gold warming all those around her,
Like the sun warming the sea.

Her dress rolling like the night sea's wave,
Her feet whisper as she glides across the ocean
Like the sea creatures calling her name,
She sways side to side,
As she walks the wind is pulling her and leading her,
The way as the tide gradually goes in further and further.

Hannah Stokes (10)
Culverstone Green CP School, Gravesend

Midnight Sky

The big, black eyes twinkle like the night sky,
Sitting on the edge of the Earth, he watches as a shooting
                                            star goes by,
As he drives into the mist, the starry necklace fades away,
When his mum starts to call, he dives into the sea,
Lost in the middle of the ocean, he dies but as this happens
                                    the midday sun appears.

Sam Bampton (10)
Culverstone Green CP School, Gravesend

The Sea

Her eyes are like blue sapphires that would sink to the
                                    bottom of the ocean,
Her wavy long hair pounds against her back like a
                                seashore being destroyed,
As she wanders forwards the feel of the sand tickles her feet,
As she glides into the distance, a new friend appears.

Kathryn Tye (10)
Culverstone Green CP School, Gravesend

The Great Blue Sea

Her hair is like the waves in the sea
Her eyes are the most sparkling pebbles on the sandy beach
She has lips as red as the sunset on the beach
Her heart is a pot of gold just been found on an island.

The sea is pounding and crashing together
As the sand sticks to her feet
As she strides along the beach her shoes glisten in the sunlight
Gradually her shadow is getting smaller when the night gets darker
As she walks into the sea, going deeper into the night.

Sophie Ballard (10)
Culverstone Green CP School, Gravesend

Frosty

Razor-sharp, white, prickly frost
Covered hair standing to attention
Like a row of soldiers
Inky-blue eyes like two ice cubes
His arms numb with the cold
Unable to bend in the bitter artic wind
His legs encrusted with ice
Unable to move away from the sub-zero temperatures.

Glen Harrison (10)
Culverstone Green CP School, Gravesend

The Silent River

His hair ripples across the rocks
He swiftly travels through the crystal clear water
When he becomes furious the rapids roar and pound against the side,
Glistening water falls down his body
The waves are controlled by him and never lost
His powerful legs kick away from the strong waves.

Oscar Saxton (10)
Culverstone Green CP School, Gravesend

The Mistress Of The Waterway

Her hair, a bluey-greeny colour, followed in long, dazzling trains.
Dress so long it gushes onto everything.
Her eyes had a mysterious blue tint to them.
The skin that she has is blue all over
And has a shining hint to it.

As she dances in the valley her hair flies about,
Her hair, dress and body are so sparkly
That you can see them for miles around.
She glistens like the sparkle from the sun.
As she flows further a huge something appears.

Adam Stonham (10)
Culverstone Green CP School, Gravesend

The Sea

Her hair flows against her back,
Her eyes twinkle like diamonds,
She rolls through the air as her necklace sparkles,
Her earrings flicker as she twirls around in the soft sand.

Her ring shines like a star as her sleeves get in the way,
As she glides along the water her golden bracelet disappears,
Her ribbon glows as she approaches the darkness,
The night falls as she fades away.

Bryony Stokes (10)
Culverstone Green CP School, Gravesend

She

Whenever she is angry, she violently pounds the seafront,
She is as powerful as the crash of a tidal wave.

Her eyes are as beautiful as the water's sparkle.
Her seaweed hair swaying with the waves.
She dances as the moonlight shines.

Matthew Coward (10)
Culverstone Green CP School, Gravesend

The Ocean Queen

Her body crashes against the rocks, as her pearl necklace
glistens in the sunlight.
Her eyes are the clear pebbles under the water.
Her voice is a thundering storm echoing through the universe.
Her hair is the never-ending waves passing through the seven seas.
Her arms are the harmless fishes pleading not to be caught.
She feels she is a dolphin diving in and out the water.
She is a ballerina dancing along the sapphire blanket.
She approaches her sea kingdom waiting for her servants.
She is now the ocean queen.

Melissa Kose (10)
Culverstone Green CP School, Gravesend

The Wild Winter

His hair is like a silk snow carpet,
His eyes are like sparkling crystal snowflakes,
His neck crackles like it's ice breaking,
His stomach clenches as one eye catches a polar bear,
His fingers so cold they are just like icicles,
His legs are like moving trees,
As he approaches a frozen lake his knees are knocking,
As his feet touch the snow it feels like a finger sticking to an ice cube.

Rebecca Pillet (10)
Culverstone Green CP School, Gravesend

The Moon Lady

Her face lit up like a veiled crystal when anyone slithered past her.
The eyes that belonged to her shone like sapphires.
Her dress came out as if to curtsey
As she strolled into the dark night mist and stopped.
Then her ribbon started to whisk up around her
Then she vanished into thin air
And the light entered the world again.

Anna Johnson (10)
Culverstone Green CP School, Gravesend

Winter's Last Flake

His hair melts away as he walks on and on whilst stabbing the
breeze with its spikes.
He has the fingernails of icicles growing sharper and sharper
until the light of the sun comes out to play.
His eyes glisten like the last fallen snowflake about to
disappear like all the rest.
The clothes that he wears are like Christmas tree lights to be taken
down when winter ends.

In the summer he fades, like the snow melts away only to be
seen once a year.
His heart freezing everything around him while it beats as every
snowflake falls.
As he wanders across the earth he inspires every mortal with his ice
crystal body to die by the light of the sun.
As he scatters to coldness as fast as ever a new face appears
to take his place.

Rickie Durnall (10)
Culverstone Green CP School, Gravesend

Stormy Weather

Showers of water waving across the road,
Misty magic bursting through the clouds,
Branches wagging like the tails of happy dogs,
Whistling, howling like wolves,
Angry faces moving swiftly across the sky,
Blustery leaves swirling madly around the playground,
Toppling bins spilling rubbish everywhere,
Grass sways in the gusts of anger,
Birds whooshing over you like jet planes,
Dull, dismal light from the sun, trying to break the clouds,
It must defeat them.

Ryan McManus (10)
East Wittering Community Primary School, Chichester

Weather Poems

Lightning lashing from the sky,
While grey clouds stay up high.

Slithering tiles falling to the ground,
As all the people watch around.

Howling wind like a dog,
Look out the window, there's the fog.

Rattling windows in the dark,
All I want to do is go to the park.

Bumpy clouds bash together,
Look outside, what horrible weather.

Amber Macdonald (10)
East Wittering Community Primary School, Chichester

Stormy Winds

Gasping winds, rattling leaves and banging doors,
Crashing pictures falling off the walls,
Trees whipped around in different directions,
Lights flickering on and off,
Clouds galloping across the open sky,
Shadows racing on the ground.

Ryan Parfoot (10)
East Wittering Community Primary School, Chichester

Stormy Nights

Stormy nights are here,
Waving grass, slamming doors,
Rain thrashing against the ground,
Branches jumping with joy,
Leaves rustling like scattered tigers.

Georgia Heath (10)
East Wittering Community Primary School, Chichester

Going Home

The clouds are black,
With evil faces looking down on me,
All the leaves are fluttering everywhere,
Like they've been set free,
My hair is whirling like a tornado,
So I can't hardly see,
I want to get home
And have a lovely hot mug of tea.

Sarah Bevis (10)
East Wittering Community Primary School, Chichester

A Stormy Day

Bad weather all around,
Strikes of lightning hit the ground,
Rumbling thunder, dancing trees,
Swaying of grass and blowing of leaves,
Blinds banging, windows creaking,
Shaking trees like a happy dog's tail,
Flashing street lights flickering.

Chloe Stanton (10)
East Wittering Community Primary School, Chichester

Weather

Teardrops trickling down madly
Bins crashing to the floor
Branches, bowing to one another
Water splashing to the ground
Gates bashing
Girls' hair swaying side to side
Black clouds building up.

Jade Hawkins (10)
East Wittering Community Primary School, Chichester

The Storm

Chains rattling in the howling wind,
Gutters overflowing in the teardrop rain,
Tree branches dancing madly to the wind,
Roof tiles are flying in the whistling wind,
Black, dark clouds look like devils' faces,
Puddles splash, a ton of rain tips down,
Lights flicker on and off,
While the evil wind blows,
Thunder is booming like a giant's voice,
Lightning flashes as quick as a jet.

Jonathan Manuel (10)
East Wittering Community Primary School, Chichester

The Storm

Sleeping storm clouds coming over,
Like the start of a new dark age,
Breathtaking to watch,
Trees shake in fear, wind picking up,
Grass started waving, shouting for help,
Birds flying madly to get away from the stormy weather,
Evil clouds smashing together,
Lights flickering in the night sky.

Charlie Ames (11)
East Wittering Community Primary School, Chichester

The Storm

The storm is huge,
It's coming out with rage,
Leaves are blown even on this very page,
Puddles are bigger, trees are shaking,
Windows rattling, pots are breaking,
Pencils rolling and acorns falling.

Gavin Ngo (10)
East Wittering Community Primary School, Chichester

Whooshing Wind

Looking out the window, lights flickering,
Trees whipping then open the window,
Smash, crash, the window shuts,
Crash, in shock the door slammed,
Wind shooting down the chimney making pictures rumble,
Wind whistling when it hits houses,
I go out to the lounge,
I can hear the verandas rattling,
The rain smashing on glass windows,
The trees look like they've been hit by hurricane Ivan,
I heard a smash, tiles came off someone's roof,
Animals yelping in the zoo,
Fences rattling,
Barbed wire whipping,
Plants being pulled from their flowerbeds,
Rabbits taking shelter behind trees in the ground.

Ben Houghton (10)
East Wittering Community Primary School, Chichester

Untitled

The terrible night
Jets of mist,
Fences rattling,
Branches snap.

The storm
Leaves whirling,
A storm is coming,
It is here.

The sea
Waves crashing,
White froth everywhere,
Surfers gone.

Billy Callow (11)
East Wittering Community Primary School, Chichester

The Weather

Doors crashing, gates banging,
Dogs barking, fences breaking,
Trees bashing, lights flickering,
Torrential rain, howling wind,
Dancing trees, blowing in the wind,
Girls' hair blowing in the wind like mad,
Boys' hats blowing in the wind, up in the trees,
The ground shakes as the storm comes,
The trees are like dancing people.

Lauren Taylor (10)
East Wittering Community Primary School, Chichester

Weather

Bold black clouds slowly building
Grey gusts of wind blowing leaves about
Heavy rain clashing against windows
Howling winds bossing leaves about
Rustling leaves waving in the air
Lights flickering, pictures falling
And crashing to the ground.

Daniel Fuller (10)
East Wittering Community Primary School, Chichester

The Storm

Trees snapping, windows flapping,
Fences smashing, thunder flashing,
Roof tiles cracking,
Windows smashing,
Wind whistling, doors banging,
Rain splashing, hitting the ground.

George Taylor (10)
East Wittering Community Primary School, Chichester

The Weather

Howling wind,
Light flashing,
The sea clashing together,
The trees clashing,
The black clouds slowly moving,
The puddles splashing,
Heavy rain blustering against windows,
Rain thudding against the ground,
Branches snapping,
Dustbin lids rolling,
Cans rolling,
Lights flickering,
Birds flying madly,
Dogs barking,
Clocks falling,
Tiles cracking.

Melissa Bearham (11)
East Wittering Community Primary School, Chichester

Weather

Thunder booming
Screaming lightning lashing down
Lamp posts flickering
Zooming fire engines
Trees bending from side to side
Dark grey clouds pouring down buckets of rain
People screaming as roofs are being whipped off houses
Branches snapping off trees then flying in the air
Wind you can see
Gigantic waves whooshing in the sea
Smashing windows as the wind's so strong
Bins crashing together.

Emma Napper (10)
East Wittering Community Primary School, Chichester

The Weather

Branches snapping, fences breaking,
Leaves falling, black clouds shading,
Bushes rustling, rain dropping,
Girls playing, boys' hats falling off,
Lights smashing,
Wind howling,
Photos dropping,
China breaking.

Sammy-Jo Valler (10)
East Wittering Community Primary School, Chichester

Rainy Days

Rain clashing like a can rolling,
Trees swaying like a puppy's tail,
Wind whistling like a howling dog,
Leaves rustling like someone falling to the floor,
Windows shaking like bars smashing to the ground,
Doors banging like a fence falling.

Alex Heath (10)
East Wittering Community Primary School, Chichester

Power Cut

Lightning flashing, thunder clashing,
Lights are out, that's when you hear the shout,
Power cut,
Windows rattling, the rain pattering,
Finding candles for light
Because it will be a pitch-black night.

Elliott Courtney (10)
East Wittering Community Primary School, Chichester

On The Way To School

Cars are caught in mud,
Doors are falling off children's houses,
Water is pitter-pattering on the patio roof,
Dark clouds covering children,
Golden curls are twisting into a whirlwind,
Pink, yellow, blue, hoods are caught on branches,
Tins are falling out of the bins,
Tumbling of rain on the window,
When you breathe, the wind catches your mouth,
Vases smashing to the ground,
Children's school books are wringing wet,
Lightning strikes the ground,
Branches move side to side,
Birds find cover,
Trees falling over,
Leaves are scattering,
Fingers are numb.

Portia Bye (10)
East Wittering Community Primary School, Chichester

The Death Of Ophelia

A pale, delicate hand
Protruded from the water
A pale, delicate face
Supported by her flowing hair
She drifted
Dreaming and chanting
Passing silent osier and weeping willow
As she floated, silently
Along the brook,
Flowing weeds slowing her
And held her in the golden stream.

Alexander Loveday (10)
Hampton Hill Junior School, Hampton Hill

The Death Of Ophelia

Ophelia is drifting along the stream
Her hair tangling with the weeds,
Her hands floating like water lilies,
The trees and plants around her
Accept her as if she is part of the stream,
As she swiftly glides through the water
She sings a song to herself,
Quietly,
Her lips hardly moving,
Her eyes almost asleep,
It is as if she is in a trance,
The air seeps through her hair,
She feels her body sinking,
Deeper and deeper,
Into the calm water,
Yet she does nothing,
But sing sweetly,
As she sinks slowly
Into the water.

Serena Dias (10)
Hampton Hill Junior School, Hampton Hill

The Death Of Ophelia

Here a ghostly body floats upon the ripples
Her long red hair weaving through the willows
The smell of hovering scent all around her
From the snowflakes, nettles and daisies
Her billowing dress drifting down the stream
The gentle breeze creating miniature waves
Drooping plants surrounding her robes
Carry her to death.

Jack Ravenscroft (10)
Hampton Hill Junior School, Hampton Hill

The Death Of Ophelia

As she drifts slowly through the muddy water
You can hear a faint melody
The smells of nature all around
Her voice is thin
As dark death closes round her
The beautiful hand-crafted dress
Sodden
Slowly taking her
To her watery grave
As she floats
The flowers in her hand droop sadly
She draws her last few breaths
To the sound of the rippling stream
Taking her to her rest.

Scott Mitchell (10)
Hampton Hill Junior School, Hampton Hill

The Death Of Ophelia

There she lies
Calm and still,
Weeping, weaving
In and out of the muddy brook,
She can smell the dampness
Of the cold weedy water.
She feels drowsy, droopy and dreamy,
The water dripping peacefully
Is what she can hear.
She can see the osier beds
Drifting past,
As she slowly is carried away
To her cold, sad death.

Harriet Thomlinson (10)
Hampton Hill Junior School, Hampton Hill

Sleeping Ophelia

As she drifts through the water
Senseless of anything around,
The birds and the bees gone quiet -
All but no noise.
Her murmuring sweet voice wafting down the river,
As if it was river's voice too.
The river entwining itself around her.
All her dress spread wide,
With her scented flowers floating,
The smell so sweet and wistfully strong,
As it twists and trails itself around the cooling air.
Her hair spirals out before her,
As if it were leading the way.
She drifts on through the brook,
Bringing gloom and anger with her,
All the way to the grave.

Georgia Cottington (10)
Hampton Hill Junior School, Hampton Hill

The Death Of Ophelia

As she floats, she slowly drifts away
Dreaming of a beautiful summer's day,
The smell of flowers as she is adrift
Takes her to a better world than this.
With only trees and fishes for her friends,
For in her heart the pain just never ends.
She feels induced into the element,
The feel of slimy weeds and scaly fishes.
Her time is nearly up, although she thinks
She can live on forever as she sings.
Slowly she goes down, lower and lower,
Even though she did not do anything,
She died a very slow and painful death.

Luke Beer (10)
Hampton Hill Junior School, Hampton Hill

The Death Of Ophelia

A glowing shadow
Clasped by nature,
Ophelia glides down
The muddy brook.
Silence,
Apart from her soft voice,
Singing the melodies of the ages.
A scent of wild flowers follows,
The wind holding her.
Her hair swaying
In the rippling water.
Her silver dress torn,
But still beautiful,
Drags her to a
Silent death with
Nature.

Susan Jonusas (10)
Hampton Hill Junior School, Hampton Hill

The Death Of Ophelia

There in the muddy brook,
Ophelia drifts into complete silence.
The drooping willow leaves,
Trailing along her body.
The feel of the cold, wet weeds,
Sludging along her arms.
The flowers in her hand,
Drifting droopily down the water,
With her senseless body.
The only smell she could smell,
Was her slow painful death,
Definitely slow and painful,
And definitely death.

Jessica Roe (10)
Hampton Hill Junior School, Hampton Hill

Ophelia's Lullaby

As she floats down the brook
The muddy water flows in and out of her mouth,
Her pale lips tasting nature.
Her mind drunk and her body almost lifeless,
She can smell the earth which lurks beneath her
And can hear the willows rustling.
She can see the green leafy Heaven above,
As her coronet slips off and glides away.
Her hands look like cloth as they swirl and touch the water.
Her body is empty.
She sings softly to herself.
Her eyes reflect the beautiful flowers
That form a bed around her.
The water tries to slyly pull her under
But she doesn't seem to mind.
There one goes,
The one who is queen of nature.
Then she disappears - her life is happier -
But her coronet is still floating.

Sophie Dexter (10)
Hampton Hill Junior School, Hampton Hill

The Death Of Ophelia

The weeds and willow grope like unseen hands
And, dreamily,
Death drags drowsily
At the dress
Of dying Ophelia,
Drifting droopily downstream,
She breaks out in song,
As delirium takes hold,
Singing for her love - lust -
Hamlet.

Adam Bassett (11)
Hampton Hill Junior School, Hampton Hill

The Death Of Ophelia

Drifting down the river
Her hair splayed beneath her head,
Singing softly, sadly, slowly . . .
Not fearing the moment she would sink,
Sink to her doom,
Distraught and deranged,
Her voice wavering,
Wavering and low.
Her dress dragging her . . .
Slowly, oh so slowly
To her death . . .
In her mind she was calm.
Not many could understand -
Not many ever would.
She would die as one with nature.
The man she loved would never know
If she had accepted his apology,
But in her mind she already had.
Alas, it was now too late . . .
The bubbling stopped,
Her mouth didn't take in the taste of water.
Hamlet's Ophelia was dead.

Thomas Gellatly (10)
Hampton Hill Junior School, Hampton Hill

The Death Of Ophelia

The cold, pale hand of a ghostly figure.
The shape of Ophelia's drenched droopy body.
Her frozen mouth slowly moving,
Remembering a song from far away.
The willow tree whispers above her emerald eyes,
Her flowing hair cushioning her fragile icy head.
The weeds send her gently slithering down,
To her wet watery grave.

George Thompson (10)
Hampton Hill Junior School, Hampton Hill

The Death Of Ophelia

The light lay from the brook
Luring me over to the side
Then - there she was
Drifting down the stream
Murmuring to herself
The sweet smell of flowers
Wafting in the air
The dripping of water
From the osier aslant the brook
She looked to be drifting
In and out of consciousness
Flowers wavering in her hands
As she slowly, softly, unpurposefully drifted on.
Her face had no expression,
The water was slowly claiming her for itself.

James Boultbee (11)
Hampton Hill Junior School, Hampton Hill

The Death Of Ophelia

A weeping willow hanging over her,
She floats so gracefully
With hair trailing behind.
The sickening smell of mud
Makes her unconscious.
She trusts nature as if it were a friend.
The water tries to help her
But it fails.
Her will to become part of nature is very strong.
She sings so weakly,
Remembering the songs,
As quietly she cries
And becomes the water.

Giada Ciccozzi (10)
Hampton Hill Junior School, Hampton Hill

The Death Of Ophelia

A ghostly body glides down a river
Floating,
Her hair tangling in the weeds
Drifting.
Emotionless.
Nothing at all.
The water rippling against her body
Drowsy, floppy.
She trails her dress.
Her head encloses some flowers.
Trees rustling.
Nothing else.
She passes a willow and lays there,
Allowing herself to drift away.
A gentle breeze blows against her frail body,
The stream carries her on and on.

Jonny Brown (11)
Hampton Hill Junior School, Hampton Hill

The Death Of Ophelia

Here she floats through a deserted river,
Weaving through willows and shifting moss,
She smells the murky water and rotten wood
And is desolate, colour drained out of her lips.
She sings holy prayers and hymns to God,
But her pale and opaque life is gone.
The nettles, daisies and weeds surround her,
Calling her theirs for eternity.
She feels not happy, not alive,
At last the muddy water takes her,
To a peaceful death.

Alex Cheah (10)
Hampton Hill Junior School, Hampton Hill

Chocolate

C hocolate is lovely and it is sweet.
H ot chocolate, yum yum, chocolate!
O h lovely chocolate, yum yum yum!
C hocolate, chocolate, lovely and sweet.
O h, oh, chocolate, it is my favourite food.
L ovely chocolate, I'll never forget what
A lovely gift. I can't wait
T ill I get some chocolate, I get so excited.
E very day I will like a piece of chocolate.

Tegan Giannandrea (8)
Hawes Down Junior School, West Wickham

Run, Run As Fast As You Can . . .

A roar of the crowd,
My mum and dad were very proud,
I looked at my teddy bear mascot,
He was my teammate from Ascot,
I looked up into the gloom then,
The gun went baboom,
I leapt off the line,
Was the gold gonna be mine?

I was Godzilla chasing a whale,
I was a frog chasing a fly,
I was a tiger chasing a deer.

Run, run, as fast as you can,
You can't catch me cos I'm a great British man.

I won the gold!
The gold was mine,
The gold was mine!
My glorious day!

Lewis Green (10)
Holy Trinity CE Primary School, Cookham

My Childhood Dream

The boom of my heart,
Like the beat of a drum,
The flash of the sun,
The roar of the crowd,
The bang of the gun.

The sound of my feet hitting the ground,
The crowd is just a blur now,
I can hear the crowd cheering me on,
I'm running, I'm running as fast as I can,
As fast as a cheetah, as fast as a train,
As fast as a cat in the rain,
I can see it, see it well, it's just up ahead,
It's glitzy and colourful,
Then I ran and ran through the line,
I have won, I have won,
I have won again.

Rebecca Price (10)
Holy Trinity CE Primary School, Cookham

Dive Bomber

I ran,
I climbed,
I jumped from the board,
Falling like a bomb heading for a town,
Then *boom!* I hit the water,
Freezing like an ice cube,
I floated to the side,
I got my towel, wrapped it round me,
Then headed for the changing room,
I went to the scoreboard and saw I was top,
Then ran to the podium for my gleaming gold.

Rhys Palmer (10)
Holy Trinity CE Primary School, Cookham

My Olympic Dream

A bang of the gun,
Off we go,
A cheer of the crowd,
My country was proud,
I ran as fast as I could.

I saw lots of faces,
And a whirl of colours,
I heard lots of people shouting
And roaring.

I was nearing the finishing line,
I reached out as far as I could,
I had just won the gold medal,
It was like a shiny new penny,
My dream had come true.

Kiren Sehota (10)
Holy Trinity CE Primary School, Cookham

My First Medal

Putting my feet on the starting line
Then I was getting ready
The gun went off
I jetted off before anyone else

I saw the spectators . . . looked like a blur
Like a piece of fur
I smelt the smell of smelly hot dogs
I heard my trainers
As they went up and down

I tasted . . . hum, I tasted nothing
I ran to touch the wall
As I was running to the wall
I was way past the finish line.

Christopher Benge (10)
Holy Trinity CE Primary School, Cookham

A Dream Came True

An applause,
Oh no! Bang!
I was off.

It was an amazing moment,
My heart thumping like mad,
The finish line increasing,
My competitors gaining.

A big bound,
Over,
Glorious gold,
Wow,
My dream came true.

Daisy Green (10)
Holy Trinity CE Primary School, Cookham

Record Breaking Race

Feet connecting to starting blocks
People getting eerier
Crowds going silent
The starting marshal loading the starting pistol

The gun went *bang*
Sprinting like a cheetah
Faster and faster like greyhounds after the rabbit
Over the finish line in the blink of an eye

Waiting for that glorious gold to be round my neck
There was a party going on inside me
A new record had been set
I felt like the tortoise after beating the hare.

Alastair Beveridge (10)
Holy Trinity CE Primary School, Cookham

My Wonderful Win!

The roar of the crowd sounded like a lion,
The deafening fight for glory.

A blurry blotch of colours and faces,
A flash of a camera coming from all places.

My legs were frozen as if they were lead,
A shot sounded which echoed in my head,
Taking me out of my thoughts.

I plunged into the water,
My heart was beating as fast as a strike of lightning,
Everything was intimidating.

I found myself with a medal around my neck,
I was speechless, I didn't even say thank you,
When someone said, 'Well done, Miss Beck!'

Jennifer Crichton (10)
Holy Trinity CE Primary School, Cookham

My Amazing Achievement

Haze of colours,
Thrilled crowd cheers,
Have the courage,
Shed no tears,
Javelin soars,
Ever so high,
Just like a starling,
Up in the sky,
Shoots back down,
Everything's quiet,
The javelin cracks the ground.

Craig Jenkins (10)
Holy Trinity CE Primary School, Cookham

My Dream Win

A glimpse of the pool,
A nervous heartbeat,
A spin of colours,
I couldn't speak.

A commentator calling names,
Deafening cheers,
Muffled sounds,
My head was going round and round.

I walked to my place,
I was feeling hot in the face,
I wasn't ready to race.

The gun went,
I dived
Under the water, I felt revived.

On my last lap,
This could be it,
On the road to the end,
I bend.

Out of the pool,
Into the changing room,
All I could feel was a zoom, zoom, zoom!

Upon the podium,
I see all of the them,
Spectators and athletes,
I had won gold,
My dream win.

Rachel Brand (10)
Holy Trinity CE Primary School, Cookham

My Own Planet

3, 2, 1, *bang!*
There goes the gunshot,
Bang! Bang!
Tension in the heart,
Boom! Boom!

Placid as a tortoise,
Smoothly moving across the track,
A pack of wolves hungry for their medal,
People scavenging for their luck.

Running, running,
Racing, racing,
Round the track,
Racing children looking for their prize.

One more lap to go,
Zoom! Zoom!
Two people in my way,
Zoom! Zoom!
One person in my way,
Zoom! Zoom!

In first place,
Flying round the track,
Nearing the line,
A collection of lights and flashes all a blur,
People screaming congratulating me,
Why do all these things occur?
Yes, I had done it, I had won it.

Awarded a golden star from a land afar,
Hung round my neck like I'm holding the world,
I wish this moment could forever freeze,
I now have a planet, especially for me.

Lizzie Davis (10)
Holy Trinity CE Primary School, Cookham

An Olympic Dream

A scream,
A shout,
A streaker about,
The sound of a gun and off we go.

A blur of the mind,
The power of my legs,
Enough to put me far ahead.

Running onwards,
Ever onwards,
The speed of a cheetah outrunning an antelope,
My heart beating in a fist of steel,
As I begin to gain hope.

A shriek from the crowd,
Exceedingly loud,
The medal looms in my mind,
Enemies coming up behind,
Run! Run! Run!

Passing through first,
The finishing ribbon,
My thoughts a swirl and now forgiven.
Picking up my home team's flag,
I've got the race in the bag!

Lindsay Coulson (10)
Holy Trinity CE Primary School, Cookham

My Glorious Gold

The crowd bellowed,
My turn now,
A bang of a gun,
Off we went.

My view a blur,
My heart alive,
Like an eagle in the sky.

Whirling wind,
In my face,
The runner behind,
She's called Stace.

I hope I win the running race,
The finish line up ahead,
A few seconds in front of Stace.

I won the gold,
I'm the best,
I can't believe I beat Stace,
The reigning champ,
She came in second place,
On the podium received my medal,
I can't believe I won gold,
My dream had become an authentic story!

Harvey Dale (10)
Holy Trinity CE Primary School, Cookham

Third Place

A cheer of my name,
A bang from a gun,
We all dive in really quickly.

A splash from all of us,
A funny kick,
Arms in the air,
I need to win, win, win!

A blur of colour as I breathe,
The wall in front of us getting near,
My tumble not so far,
One more length to go.

A race of my life,
I won't give in,
I want to win,
I need the victory,
I'm so tired, I need to stop,
But I'm racing for my life.

I stare at the screen,
I am so disappointed,
I win the bronze,
But that's okay.

Carmen Ip (10)
Holy Trinity CE Primary School, Cookham

Golden Glory!

When I splash I make a wave,
As the crowds begin to rave.
There's a big fish in the sea,
Exactly the same size as me.

As I kick my feet,
Someone else tries to cheat.
Everyone fighting for first place,
We're going at a very fast pace!

I'm battling for my very best dream
And thinking of my fave strawberries and cream.
All I see is the white, white wall,
Someone starts to splutter and stall.

There's an odour of burgers and chips,
It's making drool run from my lips.
I'm going for first
And not doing my worst.

I've touched the wall,
It was fun after all.
Here's my gold,
I'm about to explode!

Hannah Wallace (10)
Holy Trinity CE Primary School, Cookham

The Determined Hawk

Pulling back like a stretchy spring
The howl of a wolf made its call
As the lunge hit the airway before all
Its sharp swordfish tip hit the sky
As if it had wings and was able to fly
Its speed was faster than a charging bull
But still going high like a homing seagull
Soon it reached higher than the moon's moons
Higher than moving Mars
And then the last hysteric laugh of a hyena's behalf,
The sudden stop paused the world as it started to swoop down,
The determined hawk dipped,
But moved up as the wind blew,
The bird found its targeted prey,
So it set its mind on it for the day,
Burning through stiff air walls,
Feeding itself into a defenceless mouse just missing a small louse,
But the sudden smash of it hitting the ground,
Wasn't loud enough against the crowd,
Soon the medal was on my neck,
But my opponents were in a hideous wreck.

Sam Taylor (10)
Holy Trinity CE Primary School, Cookham

The Olympic Final

My feet were in the starting block
My feet started to shake
The bang of the gun
We're off

I was like a train
In the rain
There was a cheetah
There was an eagle
There was a leopard
All running beside me

I saw a multicoloured rainbow
I looked down, I saw the finish
I was staring at the line
I was getting closer and closer

I was 5m from the strip
I slipped
I felt fine
The paramedic came
I said I could carry on
Then I felt the pain.

Charlie Breden (10)
Holy Trinity CE Primary School, Cookham

My Medal

Roars of cheers echoed from the crowd,
As I looked up at the snow-white clouds,
A bang from the gun,
The race has begun.

I dive like a fish,
I give my legs a swish,
The weather is boiling hot,
I feel like I am in a cooking pot.

I start to daydream,
As cheers come from my team,
I think of the medals,
As I kick like fast bike pedals.

I want to win,
I have to win,
Has my dream come true
In this pool of blue?

I see the finish line,
As I start to whine,
I've won the silver,
My dream is over.

Michelle Watt (10)
Holy Trinity CE Primary School, Cookham

I Wish!

A flash of light,
A deafening roar,
Get ready,
Get set,
Bang!
Off we go.

The beating of a battle drum
In my ears,
In the crowd I look to see
Some people wearing smiles,
But others wearing leers.
The finish gets closer,
Then I'm past the line,
I've finally finished,
Though I haven't won.

Glinting silver medal,
Hanging round my neck,
I wish, I wish, oh how I wish,
I won and got the gold!
Now my dreams of winning
Lost forever and ever.

Elizabeth Ferguson (10)
Holy Trinity CE Primary School, Cookham

The Horror Of Losing

A chariot,
A chariot of fire,
A sprint,
A spring of life.

Out of the blocks,
As fast as you can,
You race,
You race for glory,
You race for glory,
You race.

You trip,
You skid,
You lose,
It kills,
It stings.

Hell, Hell,
It feels like Hell,
Nothing's worse,
Nothing, I tell you,
Nothing.

John Cousins (11)
Holy Trinity CE Primary School, Cookham

My Glorious Gold

A cheer of the crowd,
As I walked in,
Faces were looking at me all the time,
I heard my name being called out,
I walked up into the stadium.

Picked up the discus,
Threw it far,
It looked like a bird,
Chasing its prey.

Looked where it landed,
Looked at the board,
I was amazed,
I had won.

Walked on the podium,
Looked at the medal,
It was round my neck,
I had got the gold.

Josh Baker (10)
Holy Trinity CE Primary School, Cookham

My Dream

The bang of the gun
Told me to run
As fast as I possibly could

I was as fast as a cheetah
Running through the jungle
I was as sleek as a bird in flight

I could see the finish line
Coming closer
Closer
Closer
Closer

I pass the finish line as a smudge
Of colours
I win
My gold
My life
My dream.

Corey McAllen (11)
Holy Trinity CE Primary School, Cookham

The Ball Went Down!

I stopped,
Looked, listened,
Then I threw the ball through the air,
Like a bird struggling to fly.

Then the ball hit the ground,
Then the crowd made a deafening sound,
Like an eagle screaming out loud.

I could smell the air,
It smelt like a lovely, sweet, juicy pear.

I looked into the crowd and shut my eyes,
Was the gold going to be mine?

I opened my eyes and I was there,
On the stand waiting for my gold,
I could see over there.

They put it round my neck,
I screamed out with cheer,
The gold was mine!

Megan Treacy (10)
Holy Trinity CE Primary School, Cookham

Four Years Of Waste

My beating heart,
The crying crowd,
The whining wind.

A day,
A second,
A life.

The bang of the gun,
Racing in the red-hot sun,
The crowd, the roar,
I knew this was the end,
It was so sore.

O ccurring sadness,
L ifeless defeat,
Y ell of the victor,
M iserable thrashing,
P itiful sorrow,
I knew this was defeat,
C ould I cope?

Natan Bram (10)
Holy Trinity CE Primary School, Cookham

The Art Of The Sword

A glint,
A shimmer,
A score,
Those were the memories
That I once saw.

A roar,
A shout,
A single score,
Those were the memories
That I once saw.

A bullet,
A flash
And that was that.

A scream,
A shriek
And that was that.

A dart, a zip,
A deadly
Whip.

A cut, a slash,
A deathly
Wrap.

A clash, a bash,
A guarding
Dash.

Hiroki Takano (10)
Holy Trinity CE Primary School, Cookham

My Olympic Dream

The crowd gave off a lion-like roar,
My head then started to feel numb and sore,
As I bit my nails the gun went *bang*,
Off I went, I ran, ran, ran,
Our hearts beating like battle drums,
All the crowd were now a hum,
My legs, my legs were very sore,
But my performance was not at all poor,
I ran, I ran,
As fast as I could,
I had to win,
I hoped I would,
The gold, the gold was within my reach,
I kept going,
I heard a screech,
It was a spectator who saw
I had won the gold
And now in my hand
I hold my beautiful, wonderful gold.

Elizabeth Chalmers (10)
Holy Trinity CE Primary School, Cookham

I'd Won

A glimpse of spectators,
The blaze of the sun,
A shot of the gun,
I'm off.

As brisk as a cheetah,
As rapid as a shark,
As swift as my heart,
As I still go on.

Run, run, as fast as I can,
Flashing lights,
Heading for the finish line,
Pain killing me, can't go on.

I've finished,
I've won,
I've got the gold medal,
I've won.

Zoe Broadbent (10)
Holy Trinity CE Primary School, Cookham

Colour

Colour, colour, colouring,
Why is the world full of this thing?
On people, places, wonders you'll see,
They're all gathered here in front of me.

Why? Why? Why can we see it?
It fills up our eyes bit by bit.
Autumn, autumn, it's a wonderful time,
It makes the colour of the leaves sparkle and shine.

Joshua Palmer (10)
Middleton Cheney Primary School, Banbury

My Box Of Wonder

(Based on 'Magic Box' by Kit Wright)

I will put in the box . . .
The bloodstained poppy petals of a silent battlefield,
the joyful song of a robin on a glistening winter's morning,
the diamond dew on a stalk of grass.

I will put in the box . . .
the anger in a ravenous lion's roar,
the shining eyes of the blackest cat on the darkest night of the year,
the scent of a rose on a summer's eve.

I will put in the box . . .
the song of a hump back whale in the deepest ocean,
a glittering snowflake on the top of the world,
the boiled iron core from the middle of the earth.

I will put in the box . . .
an oasis from the Sahara desert,
a frozen candle
and the burning North Pole.

My box is made of all the life surrounding me,
the sun on top, covers what's never been uncovered before,
its sides are made of the love that flows through everybody.

I shall ride my box over the great glaciers of the South Pole,
I shall be bought home back to England by a singing sperm whale.

Christopher Pridmore (10)
Middleton Cheney Primary School, Banbury

It Can't Be . . . Can It?

A vampire creeps through the sombre gloom,
My heart beats so loud you can hear a boom
And who can tell what he's searching for.

Howling sound of the blustering wind,
It can't be a vampire - can it?
Glancing over the window sill,
But the garden outside is quiet and still.

As the vampire flits by outside my room,
I have a feeling of fear and doom.
I silently creep back to my bed,
I take off the covers and there is its head!

It can't be a vampire - can it?
The bloodstained pillow stares up at me,
The horror and fear is there for me to see.

Sharni Carrier (10)
Middleton Cheney Primary School, Banbury

Nature

You may think the world is a horrible place,
Bombs, fighting, it's such a disgrace.
But there is a bright side,
The world is a happy place,
Just look at nature right in the face.
Butterflies dancing in the sky,
Bees buzzing flower to flower,
Birds singing their nice happy tunes,
Deer scampering into the forest.
So now you know when things go bad,
Turn to nature and you won't feel sad.

Lee Harris (8)
Middleton Cheney Primary School, Banbury

My Sister's Like A German

My sister's like a German,
She can speak lots of it,
She tries to dress like a man,
And likes to sit in a pit.

My sister's like a fish monger,
She eats too much of it,
Though she really is a lot younger,
She really eats the chips.

My sister's like a mammal,
She likes a good fight,
She likes lots of animals,
She likes the bite.

Maddie Knight (8)
Middleton Cheney Primary School, Banbury

Fun Times

Splashing in our pool,
Having loads of fun,
Great at Cleethorpes,
Playing with our dogs.

Picking berries,
Walking down the beach,
Having fun at Thorpe Park,
Having the time of my life.

Now it's time, we have to go,
After having great fun,
We have to leave it there,
I never wanted to go home.

Sarah Blair (9)
Middleton Cheney Primary School, Banbury

The War Has Begun

There's a fight
In the light
That is very, very bright
Every day
People pray
They're going to be all right

People say
That if you pray
You will be OK
In the light of day
But may you be OK
In the light of day

People worry
People hurry
They're really, really worried
With people away
They don't know what to say
On this awful day

When people die
All the others cry
When people get killed
The other side are thrilled
People dying
People crying

The war has begun
The war has begun
Now it has finished
It has come to an end
When will the next one begin?
Who knows when it will begin.

Rachel Hoose (8)
Middleton Cheney Primary School, Banbury

The Trip To The Fair

I got off the bus and started to rush
I got on the train as it started to rain
I sat on my seat and began to eat
As I ate, I gazed out of my window
And saw some sheep
The next thing I knew, I fell asleep
I dreamt of my mum baking a pie
And then I awoke as I choked on a fly
Then I turned around and saw a girl holding a pear
The train then had stopped as I reached the fair.

Rebecca Hyseni (10)
Middleton Cheney Primary School, Banbury

The Volcano

The volcano was an angry giant shaking its fist,
Its voice roared like a herd of elephants charging
To a river and a thunderstorm like Hell.
Its red hair went everywhere like Medusa's snake hair,
Its eyes were staring like Jaffa casting a curse.

Olatejumola Ogunlana (8)
Rosherville CE Primary School, Gravesend

Silence

Silence looks like a streak of cold white air
Silence sounds like emptiness
Silence tastes like icy water
Silence looks like a rainbow cloud
Silence feels like being born again
Silence reminds me of shivers.

Alister Brown (8)
Rosherville CE Primary School, Gravesend

Anger

Anger is flaming red like burning hot fire.
Anger sounds like a lion roaring from afar distance.
Anger tastes like chilli peppers burning your mouth.
Anger looks like fireworks.
Anger feels like your heart burning.

Alisha Baker (9)
Rosherville CE Primary School, Gravesend

Anger

Anger is flaming red like a hot fire.
Anger sounds like steam bursting from an engine.
Anger tastes like chilli peppers burning your tongue.
Anger looks like steam coming out of your ears.
Anger feels like a hot cooker burning.
Anger reminds me of bad things.

Monica Randhawa (10)
Rosherville CE Primary School, Gravesend

Silence

Silence is the colour of
Clouds in the sky.
Silence sounds of nothing.
Silence tastes of candyfloss.
Silence feels like a bunch of yawns
And it reminds me of detention.

Matthew Ball (10)
Rosherville CE Primary School, Gravesend

Anger

Anger is flaming red like a burning fire.
Anger sounds like a stormy day.
Anger tastes like green chilli from the cabbage shop.
Anger looks like when somebody hits you.
Anger feels like you want to shout.

Harjot Bahia (9)
Rosherville CE Primary School, Gravesend

The Volcano

The volcano rumbled in the sight of a young boy
The volcano voice is like guns shooting in the world war
The volcano hair is like lava from the volcano and toxic gas
The volcano eyes are beaming rocks falling out on me.

Thomas Osmond (10)
Rosherville CE Primary School, Gravesend

The Volcano Monster

The volcano was an angry giant shaking the land.
The booming voice went 'I will swallow the land.'
Its fiery red hair was all wavy and scruffy.
The orange eyes glowed all day and all night.
The angry lips spoke the words, 'Die, die, die!'
Then all was calm, he was dead, he was extinct.

Marie-Louise Svaleng (10)
Rosherville CE Primary School, Gravesend

Love

Love is pink like a love heart
Love sounds like relaxing music
Love tastes like chocolate
Love looks like people kissing in the night
Love feels like love is all around the world
Love reminds me of my mummy and daddy kissing.

Becky Brown (10)
Rosherville CE Primary School, Gravesend

Hunger

Hunger is brown like dead grass,
Hunger sounds like the cry from a baby,
Hunger tastes like nothing,
Hunger looks like lifeless people,
Hunger feels like pain,
Hunger reminds me of people falling to pieces.

Selina Rathore (10)
Rosherville CE Primary School, Gravesend

Winter

Winter's back, as white as paper,
Its eyes sparkle in the moonlight,
Its voice is deep and gentle,
He is destructive
And he can eat people with one bite!

Martin Brown (10)
Rosherville CE Primary School, Gravesend

Anger

The volcano was an angry giant shaking its fists
Its voice roared like thunder on a rainy day
Its red hair as boiling as the hottest fire
Its eyes as red as a love heart.

Aman Oberai (10)
Rosherville CE Primary School, Gravesend

Love

Love is beautiful and bright and full of love.
Love sounds like angels going up to Heaven.
Love tastes like melting chocolate.
Love looks like two people kissing.
Love feels like happy times.
Love reminds me of beer and beds.

Jodie Felstead (10)
Rosherville CE Primary School, Gravesend

Peace

Peace is the colour white for silence.
Peace sounds like waves splashing the rocks.
Peace tastes like ice cream.
Peace looks like friends.
Peace feels as if we're in Heaven.
Peace reminds me of happiness.

Luke Mancini (10)
Rosherville CE Primary School, Gravesend

The Moon

The moon was a giant's open eye
Its voice was a small tired whisper in the night
Its white glowing hair was glowing in the night
Its eyes were like sparkling stars in the night.

Chloe Fry (9)
Rosherville CE Primary School, Gravesend

Love

Love is the colour pink
Love sounds like someone having a good time
Love tastes like chocolate
Love looks like a happy couple
Love feels like lava
Love reminds me of my family.

Maisie Osmond (9)
Rosherville CE Primary School, Gravesend

Fun!

Fun is light green like grass on a sunny day
Fun is people shouting
Fun tastes like Starburst
Fun feels like sponge
Fun reminds me of my dad.

Ashley Ollek Adams (9)
Rosherville CE Primary School, Gravesend

Hate

Hate is the colour black
Hate sounds strange
Hate tastes bitter
Hate looks like a bizarre shape
Hate feels bumpy
Hate reminds me of trouble.

Olabambo Ogunlana (10)
Rosherville CE Primary School, Gravesend

Nightmare

A nightmare is a pair of scissors slicing
My dream into pieces,
Menacing people cutting my thoughts,
Silver blades attacking my peace.

Katie Akehurst (9)
Sacred Heart School, Wadhurst

Sea

A sea is a dictionary
Spitting out lots of words
Down in the murky water lies
A treasure trove of phrases
Waves trying to spell
Thrashing out letters
Listen carefully
Hear it roaring
The definition of the sea
A large area of water.

Peter Carvalho (9)
Sacred Heart School, Wadhurst

Happiness

When I think of
Happiness
It makes me want to
Laugh!

Laughter feels so bright
And yellow
And it tastes delicious
Ice cream, chocolate
Anything
You name it
All of it
Nutritious

It makes me
Want to
Dance and sing
It makes me smile
Happily
It reminds me of the light of day
Oh, I do love being
Happy.

Lily Parham (9)
Sacred Heart School, Wadhurst

Quarrel

A quarrel is a dictionary
Full of spiteful words
A tongue-tied person
Thinking about how to retort
Hurtful and hateful phrases
Stored in a heart of steel.

Elinor Bushell (9)
Sacred Heart School, Wadhurst

Love And Sadness

Love is the colour of red,
It feels warm and cosy,
Love sounds like birds singing,
It's like a hug from Mum,
Love reminds me of my sister being born,
It tastes like melted chocolate running down my throat.

S adness is the colour of blue,
A t times it feels dry and cold,
D arkness covers me when I think about sad things,
N ine terrible thoughts come into my head,
E stimated from 0-10 it would be 0,
S ounds like crying and whimpering
S adness is my worst feeling.

Jasmine Oliver (10)
Sacred Heart School, Wadhurst

Cat

A cat is a fire
Spitting out the flames
Her eyes are glowing embers
Scratching at the burning door
Her fur is full of ashes
She hisses to defend herself.

Cameron Levy (9)
Sacred Heart School, Wadhurst

Cat

A cat is a storm
Howling outside
Bawling through the window
Thudding on the roof
Waiting to be let in.

Amalia Austin (9)
Sacred Heart School, Wadhurst

Feelings

Anger is red like a volcano,
Happiness is yellow like the sun,
Love is pink like strawberry ice cream,
Silence is silver like stars on a quiet night,
Hate is black like a crow,
Sadness is dark blue like the ocean,
Fear is white like the clouds running with the wind.

Happiness tastes like Yorkshire pudding,
Love tastes like strawberry ice cream,
Hate tastes like mushrooms,
Fear tastes like putrid food.

Sophie Rist (10)
Sacred Heart School, Wadhurst

The Sea

The sea is like a fountain pen
Colours wash up to the shore
All inky and cold
The cool breeze smudges the sand
The majestic ocean washes away the scribbles.

Rebecca Lennon (9)
Sacred Heart School, Wadhurst

Lion

A lion is the sea
It roars savagely at the beach
It pounces on the sandy shore
It slowly scratches away at the cliffs.

Ben Attenborough (9)
Sacred Heart School, Wadhurst

Sounds

Hunger sounds like a rumble,
Sadness sounds like a distant cry,
Silence sounds like wind blowing through a door,
Fear sounds like a scream coming from a gravestone,
Darkness sounds like a menacing cackle,
Anger sounds like a drum being hit as hard as possible,
Happiness sounds like a cartoon character laughing,
Love sounds like a bird singing,
Laughter sounds like a clown joking,
Hate sounds like a supersonic shout.

Anthony St John-Bond (10)
Sacred Heart School, Wadhurst

Fear!

Fear is like when you are on your own,
The creaking of the door,
Thinking spiders crawl into your bed when you're asleep.

Fear is like the howling wind, blowing and blowing,
You get numb hands and cold breath,
And under the duvet you
Wait and wait and wait.

Lauren-Nicole Little (10)
Sacred Heart School, Wadhurst

Quarrel

A quarrel is a clock,
Fighting and ticking,
Shouting and tocking,
Two big hands coming
Out to hurt you,
Striking grim words at
12 o'clock.

Holly Turner (9)
Sacred Heart School, Wadhurst

Cat

A cat is a nightmare,
Scratching in my mind,
She stalks, she pounces,
Her flickering eyes threaten me,
She bites, she hisses,
She gives her final howl before disappearing.

Eleanor Boylan (9)
Sacred Heart School, Wadhurst

Colours

Anger is purple like an exploding bomb
Happiness is blue like the sea
Love is red like a rose
Laughter is yellow like a funny joke
Hate is black like a blackboard.

Andrew Horsfall-Turner (10)
Sacred Heart School, Wadhurst

Cat

A cat is a fire
It hisses for more food
It spits out flames
Its eyes glow brightly
An inferno of fur.

William Pearson (10)
Sacred Heart School, Wadhurst

Happiness

Happiness
Is like a meadow full of flowers on a sunny day,
It's the colour of the sky in summer,
It's a hug on the highest cloud.
Happiness is a baby being born
It's a waterfall in a beautiful forest.
It reminds me of when I was little.
Its sound is laughter.
Happiness is playing with your best friend.

Oriel Bathurst (10)
Sacred Heart School, Wadhurst

Colours

Happiness is like a sea of blue when Millwall win,
Hate is the colour of revenge,
Love is red when your dad has gone away,
Anger is being hit for no reason,
Fear is like a gunshot, as white as a ghost,
Silence is like snow newly settled, as white as possible,
Laughter is being tickled, as yellow as the sun,
Sadness is when someone has died, as silent as a grave.

Joseph Sandford (10)
Sacred Heart School, Wadhurst

Happiness

Happiness is like winning a competition
Happiness is like getting your exams over with
Happiness is like playing with my kittens
Happiness is like holding your baby brother for the first time
Happiness is lying in on a Saturday
Happiness is like laughter ringing out in a playground.

Georgia Sanderson-Nash (10)
Sacred Heart School, Wadhurst

Fountain Pen

A fountain pen is the sea
Its blue inky water
Splodges against the rocks
Drawing pictures on the sand
Smooth waves scribble on the beach.

Valerie Van Riet (9)
Sacred Heart School, Wadhurst

Fire

A fire is a pair of scissors
Deadly red and steely sharp
The blaze glowing hot, silver blades
Cracks, snaps and snips.

Joshua Spencer (9)
Sacred Heart School, Wadhurst

An Animal Poem By Numbers

One is the fish that
swam in the lake.

Two is the tiger that
wanted to bake.

Three is the dog that
chased a bee.

Four is the flea beside
the sea.

Five is the cheetah that
told a lie.

Six is the bird that
couldn't fly.

Anthony Hill (10)
The Holy Family RC Primary School, Maidstone

Wonders Of The Year

January, snow falls
Covering the streets in a big white blanket.
February, very cold
Creating dangerous ice parks.
March, flowers begin to unfold
Giving colour to the dull green grass.
April, out comes all the fools
Playing jokes on everyone they meet.
May, the flowers have all opened
Blooming their colours, oh what a treat.
June, the sun gets ready to shine
To give us heat in the summertime.
July, summer has come
Where families have lots of fun.
August, the trees become bare
With lots of leaves floating in the air.
September, prepare warm clothes
For the cold is on its way.
October, the cold is here
And sneaking up the stairs.
November, you will smell lots of smoke
And see bonfires everywhere.
December, out comes all the presents
Bringing joy around the world, how pleasant.

Megan Fisher (10)
The Holy Family RC Primary School, Maidstone

Strange Life

Tired on Monday
Weak on Tuesday
Ill on Wednesday
Worse on Thursday
Better on Friday
Died on Saturday
Mummified on Sunday.

Jake Brown (10)
The Holy Family RC Primary School, Maidstone

Mad House

One is my dad shouting and screaming
Two is my cat's miaowing and sounding like a demon

Three is my mum drawing her pictures
Four is my brother playing on football pitches

Five is my grandad knocking on the door
Six is my nan that is very poor

Seven is me watching TV
Eight is my brother doing PE

Nine is my friends coming to my house
Ten is the house of a mouse.

Cameron Kellett (10)
The Holy Family RC Primary School, Maidstone

Silly People

One is the man who sat on the wall
Two is the children who played with a ball

Three is the robber who stole a book
Four is a chief who wanted to cook

Five is the girl who got lost in the mist
Six is a bully who punched with his fist

Seven is the fisherman who caught a fish
Eight is the woman who washed a dish

Nine is the boy who wanted some honey
Ten is the king who had lots of money.

Kevin Kerr (10)
The Holy Family RC Primary School, Maidstone

My School

Got up on Monday
And went to school,
I washed it down
With the swimming pool.

Got up on Tuesday
Had a bad night,
The bus came early
And gave me a fright.

Got up on Wednesday
Had a good night,
The bus was on time
And I was alright.

Got up on Thursday
I was very tired,
The bus was very late
Not what I desired.

Got up on Friday
I was wide awake,
When school was over
I set off like an earthquake.

Alex Hobbs (10)
The Holy Family RC Primary School, Maidstone

Job After Job

Training on Monday
Tutor on Tuesday
Fired on Wednesday
Waitress on Thursday
Quit on Friday
Resting on Saturday
Back on Sunday
And that is what my future holds.

Ashley Peavey (10)
The Holy Family RC Primary School, Maidstone

Months Of The Year

In January the weather's wetter
February it's not much better
In March come the spring flowers
April fools with showers
In May the weather's never sure
Come June we see the sun much more
July the weather should be nice and hot
August time we don't need to wear a lot
September there might be a slight breeze
October comes with a cough and a sneeze
November comes with dark long nights
December time, Christmas lights.

Emily Dixon (10)
The Holy Family RC Primary School, Maidstone

The Things That Come From The Sky

One is a tree that sways in the breeze,
Two is the chill that made everyone freeze.

Three is the sun that bears down on us all,
Four is the storm that can't get us in the hall.

Five is the rain that comes tipping down,
Six is the snow that swirls around and around.

Seven is the frost that covers the grass,
Eight is the sun that looks hot on the glass.

Nine is the fog that is unkindly thick,
Ten are the clouds that look as dense as a brick.

Roxanne Parker (10)
The Holy Family RC Primary School, Maidstone

Months Of The Year

January brings down the bad weather,
February, such a sad day,
March, animals are happy,
April Fools Day,
May, flowers come through,
June, the sun comes up,
July, comes the blue sky,
August, the sun stays high,
September, keep warm,
October, the wind comes through,
November, the fireworks shoot up,
December, here comes Christmas.

Samuel Cooksley (10)
The Holy Family RC Primary School, Maidstone

In Spring

S melling roses is so much fun,
P erhaps I'll pick some for my mum.
R oses come in many colours,
 I n spring, delightful things.
N othing better than a thing.
G ood things happen in spring.

Aliye Aker (10)
The Holy Family RC Primary School, Maidstone

Silence

It feels like children being calm.
It looks like people sleeping.
It reminds me of splashing waves.
It sounds like raindrops falling.
It tastes like quiet in your throat.
It smells like children playing.

Verity McGhie (8)
West Hove Junior School, Hove

Darkness

It smells like red eyes lurking in the dark corners of the world,
It feels like cold blood oozing out your body,
It reminds me of heads stuck in cobwebs,
It sounds like a dose of blood.

Alex Goodger-Marsh (7)
West Hove Junior School, Hove

Thirst

It smells like the Antarctic going down my throat.
It feels like ice-cold water but never to be reached.
It reminds me of ice freezing me to death.
It tastes like the sun melting the ice in the world.
It looks like yetis taking over the world with ice.

Charlie Byard (7)
West Hove Junior School, Hove

Fun

It reminds me of a fast roller coaster
It sounds like a shining harp singing a song
It feels like the sea splashing
It looks like the teacups going really fast
It tastes like yummy pink candyfloss.

Sommer Ballagher (7)
West Hove Junior School, Hove

Fun

It sounds like a fun merry-go-round.
It looks like a sparkling star.
It feels like cold ice cream trickling down my mouth.
It reminds me of candyfloss.
It tastes of candyfloss rumbling in my tummy.

Isobel Crookston (7)
West Hove Junior School, Hove

Silence

It sounds like people fast asleep.
It reminds me of stars in the sky.
It looks like thin air.
It smells like being tired.
It tastes like fresh air.

Lois Selmes (7)
West Hove Junior School, Hove

Silence

It smells like shells on the hot sunny beach.
It feels like a hot bubble bath.
It reminds me of a big fluffy dog barking.
It sounds like some coins rattling in my purse.

Nancy Wheeler (7)
West Hove Junior School, Hove

Fear

Fear is blue like ice glittering
It looks like blue disco lights shining very brightly
It sounds like sad music
It reminds me of dripping rain from the gutter
It tastes of salt water from the sea.

Billy Davis (7)
West Hove Junior School, Hove

Thirst

It looks like smooth sand on the beach.
It feels like bubbles running down my throat.
It reminds me of the shower storming down.
It tastes like cold water struggling down my throat.

Sam Cissell (7)
West Hove Junior School, Hove

Sadness

Sadness is pale blue
Like someone dying
It tastes like a block of ice
Going down your throat
It sounds like people crying
It feels like a flower being squashed
It smells like a dead person.

Harry Harris (7)
West Hove Junior School, Hove

Darkness

It looks like a cage of Hell,
It feels like sharp claws ripping through your head,
It sounds like dispatching screams,
It smells like fresh flesh,
It reminds me of death,
It tastes like Hell itself.

Joe Miller-Marshall (8)
West Hove Junior School, Hove

Thirst

It feels like emptiness in my belly.
It sounds like fizzy Fanta.
It smells like trash in a lorry.
It reminds me of my best hot holiday.
It tastes like a burning hot sun.
It looks like raging waves.

Michael Gaffney (7)
West Hove Junior School, Hove

Noise

Noise is red, yellow and orange like a big bang,
It reminds me of going shopping,
It sounds like a car crash,
It smells like melting plastic,
It looks like burning fire,
It tastes like smelly breath,
It feels like you've been pushed over in a busy playground.

Isaac Squires (8)
West Hove Junior School, Hove

Darkness

It sounds like giant devils ripping up the trees,
It looks like glowing ghosts that are creaking up the stairs,
It feels like potion running down my throat,
It reminds me of skeletons kicking my face,
It smells like alien goo trailing up the mountains,
It tastes like blood that's just burst out of my veins.

Ethan Berry (7)
West Hove Junior School, Hove

Silence

It looks like children reading books.
It feels like devils around my bed.
It smells like burning hot flames.
It sounds like clouds floating around.
It reminds me of dolphins jumping out of the sea.
It tastes like raindrops falling.

Violet McGhie (8)
West Hove Junior School, Hove

Sadness

Sadness is blue
Like the deep blue ocean sinking through my skin
It feels like a slithering snake rushing down my body
It reminds me of the night sky
It looks like a chunk of see-through ice, cold as crystal
It tastes like sour bubblegum stuck in my mouth
It smells like sour blueberries spreading through the air
It sounds like crying drifting through my ears.

Jade Ford (7)
West Hove Junior School, Hove

Laughter

Laughter is yellow, it's like a bang of happiness
It feels like smelly hot breath
It reminds me of a train's smoke coming out of the funnel
It looks like a strange cloud up in the sky
It tastes like a flaming hot drink of lemonade
It smells like a stinky bomb just landed
It sounds like the wind blowing me forwards.

Matthew Mill (7)
West Hove Junior School, Hove

Darkness

Darkness is black like giant spiders
It feels like scary monsters killing me
It reminds me of hating people
It looks like some old big giant
It tastes like sick pork.

Noshin Ahmed (7)
West Hove Junior School, Hove

Joy

Joy is yellow,
The yellow of a spring morning,
Joy is like a sheep jumping over a hill,
It feels like a beautiful bird gliding through the sky,
It reminds me of a peaceful garden,
It looks like children playing,
It tastes like cold air,
It smells like potatoes,
It sounds like a whale singing.

Layla Sattar (8)
West Hove Junior School, Hove

Hate

Hate is black like black blood.
It reminds me of death.
It feels like squelchy mud.
It tastes like rotten eggs.
It smells like rotten fish.
It sounds like a scream.

Jay Fry (7)
West Hove Junior School, Hove

Happiness

Silver and gold sparkling in the sky
It feels like a twinkling star looking at me
It tastes like fizzy lemonade on my tongue
It looks like the moon gazing at me in bed
It smells like roses on a sunny day
It sounds like snowflakes all around.

Sophie Odwell (7)
West Hove Junior School, Hove

Laughter

Laugher is yellow
Like a great big bang of happiness
It reminds me of a funny clown
It feels like a tremendous tickle
It looks like a yellow blast of joy
It tastes like a bottle of soda
It smells like squishy banana,
It sounds like a tiny, tiny mouse laughing.

Charlie Holden (7)
West Hove Junior School, Hove

Sadness

Sadness is blue like raindrops dashing down to the ground, *splash*
It feels like some sheep in the meadow with no coat on in the cold
It smells like disgusting food that is rotten
It sounds like some volcanoes exploding
It tastes like rotten food that no one has eaten
It reminds me of someone dead.

Alice Cropper (7)
West Hove Junior School, Hove

Hate

Hate is red like bubbling, scrambled-up fire.
It feels like a hot explosion coming into my hands.
It reminds me of hot bubbles made of fire.
It looks like a giant smashing a traffic jam.
It tastes like bubbling hot potions.
It smells like rotten goo.

Louis Howell (7)
West Hove Junior School, Hove

Anger Is . . .

Anger is the colour of a ghostly night
It sounds like a wolf howling at the moon
It tastes like a poison
And it smells like a scrap heap
It looks like a storm flooding the town
It feels like a prickly bush
And it reminds me of a bat in the dark, spooky night.

Joe Pearce
West Hove Junior School, Hove

Sadness

Sadness is blue
Like candy melting in my mouth
It feels cold, horrid, sad and loud
It reminds me of tears dripping down my skin
It looks like blue rain
It smells like blueberries
It sounds like crying.

Ellie Drakeford (8)
West Hove Junior School, Hove

Love Is . . .

Love is the colour red like a rosy red rose
Love sounds like a keyboard in my head
Love tastes like sweet chocolate in my mouth
Love smells like a pleasant perfume smell
Love looks like a cat purring on a mat
Love feels like a soft silk on my eyes
Love reminds me of my cat nudging me on the cheek.

Samantha Francis (7)
West Hove Junior School, Hove

Love Is . . .

Love is red like hearts filling the air
It sounds like tinkling music in the middle of my ears
Love tastes like cake in my tummy
It smells like chocolate coming to me
It looks like hearts on a Valentine card
Love feels like the hot sun on my face
It reminds me of warmth in my body.

Millie Millington (7)
West Hove Junior School, Hove

Sadness

Sadness is blue like melting ice.
It looks like icebergs cracking.
It sounds like children crying.
It tastes like sick.
It feels like losing my best thing.
It reminds me of going to hospital.
It smells like smelly fish.

Lauren McKinnon (7)
West Hove Junior School, Hove

Silence

Silence is white like a silent cloud floating in the sky
It smells like fresh air flying through the window
It feels like nobody is around you
It looks like angels flying through the heavens
It sounds like you're lying in bed with your earmuffs on
It reminds me of sleeping in my bed at night
It tastes like oxygen floating in your mouth.

Natasha Wilcock (8)
West Hove Junior School, Hove

Laughter

Laughter is yellow like a jumpy joke.
It smells like a rose.
It sounds like a good friend.
It feels like your tummy's in knots.
It tastes like lemonade.
It reminds me of holidays.
It looks like fun!

Madelyn Arlidge (7)
West Hove Junior School, Hove

Anger

Anger is like a prickly rose.
It feels rough and spiky too.
It sounds like stamping.
It smells like smelly socks.
It reminds me of a red box exploding.

Ruhina Meah (7)
West Hove Junior School, Hove